Vibrations and waves

Advanced Physics Project for Independent Learning

Student's Guide

John Murray
in association with
Inner London Education Authority

Introduction to the Unit

This is one of the four second level APPIL Units. You will study the properties of vibrating systems and how such vibrations lead to the propagation of waves.

Your study of waves started in the first level Unit *Wave properties,* and will be completed in this Unit as you examine wave effects produced by waves originating from mechanical vibrations (e.g., sound waves) and also waves produced by vibrating electric and magnetic fields (e.g., light, radio waves).

Chapter 1 contains investigations of vibrating systems leading to an analysis of simple harmonic motion and a consideration of forced vibrations and resonance.

Chapter 2 considers the speed of propagation of waves in vibrating systems, stationary wave patterns in strings and air columns and the principles involved in producing sound in musical instruments.

Chapter 3 examines interference and diffraction of light waves and the production of optical spectra, and indicates how these phenomena provide valuable methods of measurement and analysis.

Chapter 4 considers the nature of electromagnetic waves, examines polarisation effects and compares the properties of waves in different regions of the electromagnetic spectrum.

Extensions

Extensions are provided for several reasons.

(a) To provide additional material of general interest, e.g. applications.

(b) To provide more detailed treatment of some topics.

(c) To provide additional topics, or extensions of core material, to cover the requirements of a particular examination board. In this case, the section is marked SYLLABUS EXTENSION and will be essential study for some students, although others may find it of value.

Organising your study

The aims and objectives of each chapter are particularly important in organising your learning because they tell you what you should be able to do at the end of each chapter. Use these objectives in making any summary notes you think you require to supplement answers to study questions and other questions. Try to answer the questions on objectives at the end of each chapter without referring to the Unit or your reference texts, so that the questions will provide a way of assessing whether you have achieved the required objectives.

Activities

Remember this is a course in which you learn through a variety of activities. You learn by:

reading the Unit text and reference books;

answering questions, which may involve you in the development of an idea, test the understanding and application of your knowledge, or guide your use of books and other resources;

doing the experiments, instructions for which are provided at the back of this book;

using the audio-visual material and the *computer program* included in this Unit.

Organising your time

Use the information at the opening of each chapter to organise laboratory work in the best sequence. The *progress monitor* will help you to plan your work so that you complete it in the recommended study time, which assumes that you spend 8 to 10 hours each week on physics.

You should spend between 6 and 8 weeks on this Unit, divided roughly as follows.

Chapter 1   2 weeks
Chapter 2   2 weeks
Chapter 3   2½ weeks
Chapter 4   1 week

Contents

Mechanical vibrations

Aim

The aim of this chapter is to enable you to acquire an understanding of the behaviour and properties of vibrating systems. To achieve this you will investigate experimentally a series of such oscillators, obtain an expression for the equation of motion of an oscillator and consider the effect of damping forces on the system.

Right. The Tacoma Narrows bridge collapsing as a result of wind induced oscillations.

Chapter 1

Objectives

When you have completed the work in this chapter you should be able to:

1   Use the following scientific terms correctly: damping, critical damping, isochronous, free vibration, forced vibration, natural frequency.

2   Define and use the following terms: simple harmonic motion, resonance.

3   Recognise simple examples of vibrating systems and identify the factors determining the frequency (i.e. the inertia of the system and the restoring forces acting, such as elastic and/or gravitational forces).

4   Use a geometrical model to link circular motion with simple harmonic motion.

5   Draw and interpret graphs to show the variation with time of displacement, velocity, acceleration and force for a body which is performing simple harmonic motion.

6   In simple examples, derive from first principles an expression for the period of vibration of bodies which are performing simple harmonic motion.

7   Explain the energy changes that occur when a body performs simple harmonic motion and draw and interpret graphs to show how the potential and kinetic energies of an oscillator vary with time and displacement.

8   Recall and use the equations for simple harmonic motion.

9   Solve problems on simple harmonic motion involving (i) period of vibration, (ii) energy changes.

10   Describe and explain the effect of damping on the amplitude of a system which is vibrating.

11   Distinguish, by reference to a vibrating system, between free and forced vibrations.

12   Describe and explain a vibrating system which illustrates forced vibrations and resonance (for example, Barton's pendulums).

13   Recognise and explain examples of resonance in different branches of physics.

14   EXTENSION
Describe and explain an experiment to determine g, the acceleration due to gravity.

15   EXTENSION
Solve the second order differential equation for simple harmonic motion.

Study time: 2 weeks

Experiments in chapter 1

VW 1 Motion of vibrating systems
(1½ hours)
VW 2 Effect of damping on a vibrating system
(1 hour)
VW 3 Barton's pendulums
(½ hour)
VW 4 An investigation of resonance
(1½ hours)
VW 5 Coupled pendulums
(½ hour)

References

Akrill	Chapter 15
Bolton	Chapter 4
Duncan MM	Chapter 8
Millar	Chapter 22
Nelkon	Chapters 2, 24
Wenham	Chapters 18, 19, 20, 21
Williams	Chapters 15, 16
Whelan	Chapters 10, 11

1.1 Vibrating systems

Introduction

Waves are often produced by vibrations, so this first chapter deals with this topic.

Systems which move to and fro, that is, vibrate or oscillate, are very common in science and everyday life. The pendulum of a clock and the balance wheel of a watch move in such a way; the diaphragm of a loudspeaker vibrates; atoms in molecules oscillate and electric charges oscillating in an aerial radiate electromagnetic waves.

All these and many other types of vibrations can be described by the same mathematical equations, even though the physical situations are completely different. This illustrates the power of mathematics in physics: if you remember a few equations and understand how to apply them you can solve a wide range of problems including some you have never met before.

In this chapter, after a brief look at several vibrating systems, you will derive these important equations, and see how they relate to different physical situations. You will also consider the loss of energy from any vibrating system (damping) and the way a system tends to vibrate at a particular frequency (its natural frequency). All these ideas have important applications in real life situations, and involve crucial theoretical concepts.

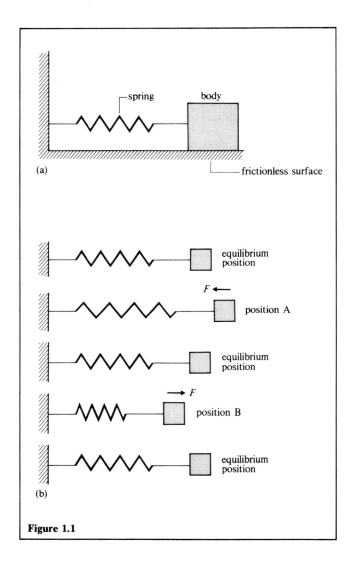

Figure 1.1

Mass on a spring

Let us first consider a simple form of mechanical vibrating system—a mass attached to a spring (figure 1.1a). When the mass is pulled to position A (figure 1.1b) and then released, there is a force (called the restoring force) which causes the mass to accelerate towards the equilibrium position. The mass goes past its equilibrium position, slows down, comes momentarily to rest at B and then repeats the motion in the opposite direction.

Q 1.1 Self-assessment question
(a) Why does the elastic restoring force decrease as the mass approaches the equilibrium position?
(b) Why does the mass overshoot the equilibrium position?
(c) Why does the mass slow down when it has gone past the equilibrium position?
(d) The energy of the vibrating system is in two parts: (i) the kinetic energy of the moving mass, and (ii) the potential energy stored in the spring. How does each of these forms of energy change as the mass vibrates to and fro?
(e) Why does the motion of the mass eventually cease?∎

The answers you have given to question 1.1 are similar to those that would be given for other oscillating systems, such as those shown in figure 1.2. These may appear very different, but they all have the same sort of motion.

E Experiment VW 1
Motion of vibrating systems
The aim of this series of experiments is to find the properties common to some vibrating systems.

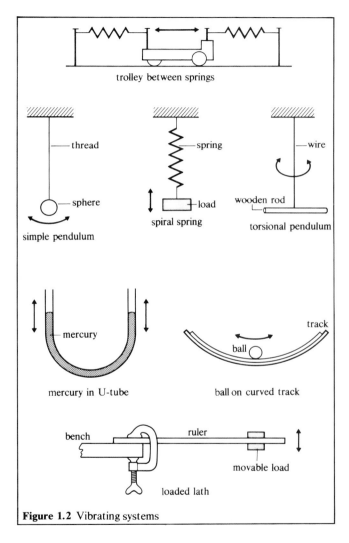

Figure 1.2 Vibrating systems

(labels within figure:)
trolley between springs
thread
sphere
simple pendulum
spring
load
spiral spring
wire
wooden rod
torsional pendulum
mercury
mercury in U-tube
track
ball
ball on curved track
bench
ruler
movable load
loaded lath

Properties of vibrating systems

From your experimental observations you should have found out some interesting information about vibrating systems (oscillators).

1   In some instances the periodic time was independent of amplitude. These are examples of a type of motion known as simple harmonic motion (s.h.m.), the definition of which will be given later. (The simple pendulum has s.h.m. only for small amplitudes.)

2   The time-trace of the motion (that is, the way in which the displacement varied with time) looks like a *sine curve*. The photograph (figure 1.3) shows a stroboscopic picture of a mass vibrating or oscillating on a spring. The camera, which was moving horizontally at constant velocity, took a series of pictures at regular intervals.

3   The periodic time of a vibrating system was dependent upon the mass of the system and the forces which were acting on it.

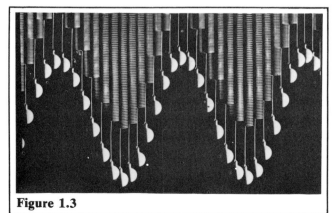

Figure 1.3

Q **1.2 Self-assessment question**
In the arrangement of figure 1.4, which system has the shortest and which has the longest time of vibration? Give reasons for your answer. (Assume that the springs are identical.)■

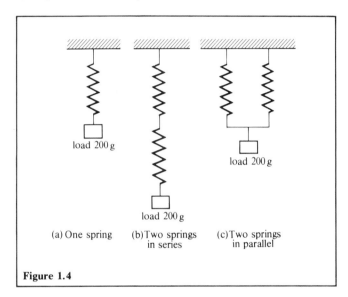

load 200 g

load 200 g

load 200 g

(a) One spring   (b) Two springs in series   (c) Two springs in parallel

Figure 1.4

Q 1.3 Development question*

This question is about the reasons why some oscillators have a periodic time which is independent of amplitude. Consider a mass on the end of a vertical spring. For most springs, the stretching force is proportional to the displacement (Hooke's law—see the Unit *Material properties*). This law is followed only if you do not over-stretch the spring. If the mass is given a small displacement and then released, it will oscillate, taking a certain time to go from the extreme position to the centre of the motion (one quarter of a period). Suppose that it is now given twice the initial displacement.

(a) Why is the average restoring force doubled?

(b) How does the average acceleration during the first quarter of a period compare with the original case?

(c) How does the average velocity of the mass compare?

(d) Explain why the mass takes the same time to travel twice the distance.■

Q 1.4 Self-assessment question

Figure 1.5a shows a trolley tied by two springs, and its displacement–time graph. Figure 1.5b shows the same trolley, with different springs. It oscillates with twice the frequency it had in figure 1.5a.

(a) Are the springs in figure 1.5b stiffer or weaker than those in figure 1.5a?

(b) In figure 1.5b the oscillation time is halved. For comparable positions, how does the speed of this second oscillator compare with that of the first oscillator?

(c) The speed of the second oscillator must be attained in half the time taken by the first oscillator. How do the accelerations of the two oscillators compare?

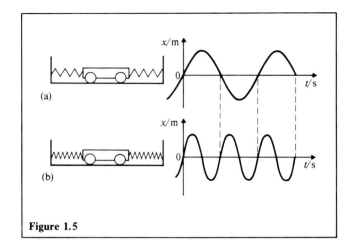

Figure 1.5

(d) The force F which the springs exert on the trolleys is given by the expression

$$F = k\,x$$

where k is the force constant and x is the displacement. If the masses of the two trolleys are the same, how do the force constants (spring stiffnesses) compare?

(e) If T is the oscillation time, which relationship below agrees with the answer to (d)?

$$T \propto k^2 \qquad T^2 \propto k \qquad T \propto \frac{1}{k^2} \qquad T^2 \propto \frac{1}{k}$$

(f) To decrease the oscillation time by changing the mass of the trolley, would one *increase* or *decrease* the mass?

(g) The answers to (a) to (c) above show that halving the oscillation time means quadrupling the acceleration, or that doubling the time means having one quarter the acceleration. How would the mass have to be changed to achieve one quarter the acceleration (and so twice the oscillation time)?

(h) Which of the following relationships agrees with the answer to (g)?

$$T^2 \propto m \qquad T \propto m^2 \qquad T^2 \propto \frac{1}{m} \qquad T \propto \frac{1}{m^2} \quad ■$$

1.2 Simple harmonic motion

Introduction

This is the name given to a type of motion which can be described by a particular set of equations and many vibrating systems perform this kind of motion.

It is *harmonic* because it keeps repeating the same pattern, and *simple* because it is physically and mathematically straightforward.

Figure 1.6 represents a body vibrating in a straight line between A and B. Two positions of the body, X, are marked. The body could be a mass attached to a spring. In this type of motion the displacement, velocity, and acceleration are constantly changing in magnitude and direction. When the mass moves up and down the restoring force is always directed towards the equilibrium position.

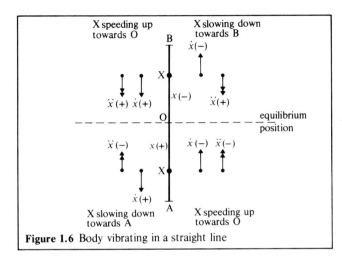

Figure 1.6 Body vibrating in a straight line

Thus the acceleration, which is proportional to the force, must also be directed towards the equilibrium position. The sign convention adopted is that quantities which are directed *downwards* are *positive* and those directed *upwards* are *negative*.

Notes: 1   In this chapter we will express the acceleration in calculus notation as

$$\text{acceleration} = \frac{\mathrm{d}^2x}{\mathrm{d}t^2} = \ddot{x}$$

This is to avoid confusion with the use of the symbol *a* for amplitude. (Text books differ in their use of symbols for equations of s.h.m.—watch out for this.)

2   Velocity may be expressed as

$$\text{velocity} = \frac{\mathrm{d}x}{\mathrm{d}t} = \dot{x}$$

Q **1.5 Self-assessment question**
(a) What is the magnitude and direction of (i) the displacement x, (ii) the velocity $\dot{x}$, and (iii) the acceleration $\ddot{x}$ at the positions O, A and B?
(b) What is always true about the relation between the displacement and the acceleration?■

Q **1.6 Development question***
In this question we will analyse the motion of a mass attached to a spring. (The same approach can be used for any system which moves with simple harmonic motion.) We will assume that the spring has negligible mass and obeys Hooke's law.
(a) In figure 1.7a the mass is at rest. What is the force exerted on the mass by the spring?
(b) Figure 1.7b shows the spring displaced a distance x from the equilibrium position and the mass moving upwards. The tension in the spring is T_1.

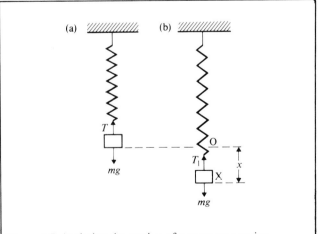

Figure 1.7 Analysing the motion of a mass on a spring

(i) Is the resultant force which is acting on the mass directed upwards or downwards?
(ii) What is the magnitude of the resultant force?
(iii) What happens to the magnitude of this force as the mass approaches O?
(c) Show that the *magnitude* of the *additional* tension is given by

$$T_1 - mg = kx$$

where k is the force constant of the spring (i.e. the force per unit extension).
(d) Show that the *magnitude* of the acceleration of the mass at X is given by

$$\ddot{x} = \frac{kx}{m}$$

(e) Is the acceleration of the mass upwards or downwards? What happens to the magnitude of the acceleration as the mass approaches O?■

The acceleration and displacement are in opposite directions and this must be taken into account in the equation. Therefore we write

$$\ddot{x} = -\frac{kx}{m}$$

where the negative sign indicates that the acceleration is in the direction opposite to that of the displacement.

An equation of simple harmonic motion

The above equation represents mathematically the motion of the mass and it is one form of the equation which represents simple harmonic motion.

Q 1.7 Self-assessment question

Complete the following statements (in words, not symbols).

(a) The acceleration is directly proportional to ———.

(b) The acceleration is always directed towards ———. ■

Any vibrating system which has these features can be represented by an equation of motion of the form

$$\ddot{x} = -c\,x$$

where c is a positive constant. To indicate that c is *positive* it is often written as ω^2 (which cannot be negative).

Thus

➡ $$\ddot{x} = -\omega^2 x$$

This is the standard form of the *equation* of s.h.m.

Q 1.8 Study question

(a) Write out and learn a definition of simple harmonic motion.

(b) Explain the meaning of the terms amplitude, period and frequency. ■

Q 1.9 Self-assessment question

What kind of motion would you expect if an object moved in such a way that its acceleration $\ddot{x}$ is related to its displacement x by the equation

$$\ddot{x} = \omega^2 x \qquad ■$$

The solution of the equation of s.h.m., that is the relationship between displacement and time, can be obtained by calculus methods.

EXTENSION

Q 1.10 Study question

If you understand differential and integral calculus, consult one of the references and follow the argument. It is a good example of a procedure which is very important in mathematical physics, namely, solving an equation (often a differential equation) which has been set up as a mathematical model of a physical situation. ■

If your mathematics is not strong, you may prefer to approach the problem by linking circular motion with simple harmonic motion. This is just a special way to solve the equation which works in this case.

Circular motion and s.h.m.

At first it may seem strange to think that simple harmonic motion is related to motion in a circle. Consider the experimental arrangement in figure 1.8. A shadow of the ball is cast on the screen. If the ball is moving steadily in a circle, the shadow will move to and fro. What do you think the motion might be? The next question shows how to find the answer.

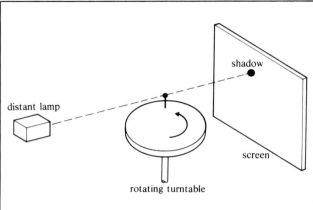

Figure 1.8 Relating circular motion and simple harmonic motion

Q 1.11 Development question

In this question you will use a geometrical model to find out something about simple harmonic motion. Suppose that a point P moves in a circle of radius a at a steady angular velocity ω. N is the foot of the perpendicular from P to the diameter AOB of the circle (figure 1.9a).

(a) Describe the motion of N as P moves round the circle.

(b) What is the acceleration of P in terms of the amplitude a of the motion and ω? In which direction is this acceleration?

(c) Assuming that $t = 0$ when $\theta = 0$ (i.e. $t = 0$ when the point N is at the centre of the line AB), show that after a time t: (i) θ is equal to ωt; (ii) the displacement x of the point N is given by $x = a \sin \omega t$.

(d) The acceleration of N is the component of the acceleration of P parallel to AB (figure 1.9b). (i) Show that the acceleration of N is given by $\ddot{x} = -a\omega^2 \sin \omega t$. (ii) What does the negative sign indicate?

(e) Because x is equal to $a \sin \omega t$ we can write

$$\ddot{x} = -\omega^2 x$$

What does this tell us about the motion of N?

(f) When is the acceleration of N (i) zero, and (ii) a maximum?■

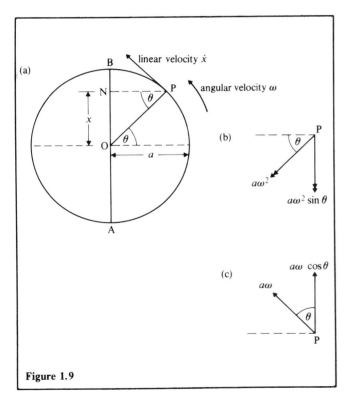

Figure 1.9

Q 1.12 Development question

Show that the period T of N, that is the time taken for N to go from A to B and back again (a cycle), is given by

$$T = \frac{2\pi}{\omega} \quad ■$$

Q 1.13 Development question

(a) The velocity of N is the component of the velocity of P parallel to AB (figure 1.9c). Again assume that $t = 0$ when $\theta = 0$. Show that the velocity of N is given by

$$\dot{x} = a\omega \cos \omega t$$

(b) When is the velocity of N (i) zero, and (ii) a maximum?■

Q 1.14 Study question

Show that we can also write the velocity of N in the form

$$\dot{x} = \pm \omega \sqrt{(a^2 - x^2)}$$

(*Hint*: $\sin^2 \theta + \cos^2 \theta = 1$, where θ is any angle.)■

The mathematical model that has been considered shows that when a point moves in a circle with a steady speed, the projection of that point on to a diameter of the circle moves with simple harmonic motion. Uniform circular motion projected perpendicularly on to any straight line produces s.h.m. The model enabled us to find the way in which the acceleration, velocity and displacement varies with time for a body which is moving with s.h.m. All these results can also be obtained by calculus.

Q 1.15 Self-assessment question

(a) Write down equations to show how, in s.h.m., (i) displacement, (ii) velocity and (iii) acceleration vary with time.

(b) Write down equations to show how (i) velocity and (ii) acceleration vary with displacement.■

You should make sure you know these equations and the significance of each one.

Note: This is simply one possible set of equations, for the case $t = 0$ when $x = 0$ (another possible set of equations is introduced in question 1.20).

Q 1.16 Self-assessment question

Draw sketch graphs to show how the displacement, velocity and acceleration of N vary with time during two complete cycles.■

Q 1.17 Self-assessment question

Draw a graph to show how the acceleration of N varies with displacement.■

Q 1.18 Study question

Using one or more of the references given at the beginning of the chapter, explain the meaning of the statement 'an important property of s.h.m. is that the motion is isochronous'. Make whatever notes you need about this topic.■

Q 1.19 Self-assessment question

A particle describes s.h.m. in which the displacement is given by

$$x = (0.05 \text{ m}) \sin 4\pi t$$

(a) What is the amplitude of the motion?
(b) What is the period of the motion?
(c) What is the maximum velocity of the particle?
(d) What is the maximum acceleration of the particle? ■

In our analysis of s.h.m. so far the time t was zero when the point N was at the centre of the line AB, the midpoint of the oscillatory motion, that is, when the displacement x was zero. However, we could have made the time zero when the displacement was a maximum, equal to the amplitude a of the motion (when N was at A or B in figure 1.9a), or some other value.

Q 1.20 Self-assessment question

Following the procedure used before, find the displacement–time, velocity–time, and acceleration–time relationships of a body performing s.h.m. for the case when the time t is zero at maximum displacement. ■

Phase

You should by now have realised that when a body is oscillating with s.h.m. the displacement, velocity and acceleration vary sinusoidally with time and that each of these quantities has a maximum value at a different time during a cycle of the motion. The velocity is a maximum when the acceleration is zero and *vice-versa*. They are out of step, and we say that there is a *phase difference* between them.

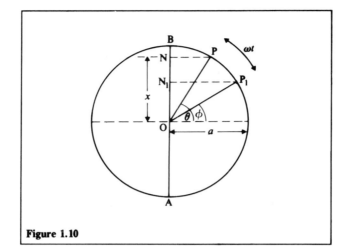

Figure 1.10

Q 1.21 Self-assessment question

Referring to your answers to question 1.16, what are the *phase difference* and the *time difference* between (i) the velocity and displacement, (ii) the velocity and acceleration, and (iii) the acceleration and displacement? ■

Suppose that we decide to measure the time from the instant when the point N goes through some other point, say N_1, between A and B (figure 1.10). How can we represent this fact in our displacement–time equation? The displacement x is given by $x = a \sin \theta$.
Because the time is now measured from the instant when OP coincides with OP_1, θ is no longer equal to ωt.
In time t the angle swept out by OP is ωt.

Thus $\quad \theta = \omega t + \phi$
Therefore $\quad x = a \sin (\omega t + \phi)$

The angle ϕ is the phase constant and indicates the phase of the motion. It is determined by the instant in the motion from which the time is measured.

Q 1.22 Self-assessment question

Figure 1.11 shows how the displacement varies with time for a point moving with s.h.m.
The equation is $x = a \sin \omega t$.
(a) What is the value of t at O_1 (use $T = 2\pi/\omega$ for a complete cycle)?
(b) Suppose the time had been measured from O_1 instead of O as the origin. What would the equation be in this case (use t_1 instead of t)?
(c) Write down a simple equation connecting t and t_1.
(d) Substitute this expression for t in $x = a \sin \omega t$ and verify that it leads to the same answer as you got in part (b). ■

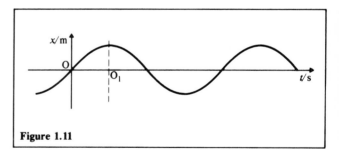

Figure 1.11

Q 1.23 Self-assessment question

Explain why a graph of $x = a \sin (\omega t + \phi)$ is the graph of $x = a \sin \omega t$ displaced *to the left* by a time interval ϕ/ω. ■

Problem solving

We will now reconsider the motion of a mass on the end of a spring to answer two questions. Is the motion simple harmonic? If so, how does the constant ω^2 relate to the physical quantities of the vibrating system?

This method can be used for any mechanical vibrating system, so make sure you understand it.

Step 1 Consider the system displaced x from its equilibrium position (refer back to figure 1.7).

Step 2 Evaluate the restoring force in terms of displacement.

Step 3 Apply Newton's second law (force = mass $\times$ acceleration) in a specified direction.

Step 4 See if the equation of motion is of the form

$$\ddot{x} = -\omega^2 x$$

Q 1.24 Development question
Steps 1 and 2 were done in question 1.6.
(a) Apply Newton's second law and show that

$$\ddot{x} = -\frac{kx}{m}$$

(b) Compare this with the standard equation for s.h.m. and say whether you think the motion of the mass on the end of a spring is s.h.m. Give your reasons.
(c) How does ω^2 relate to the physical quantities of the vibrating system?∎

Q 1.25 Self-assessment question
(a) What are the two physical quantities that determine the period of motion?
(b) Show that the dimensions of k/m are equal to the dimensions of ω^2.
(c) Write down an expression for the period of motion T in terms of the two physical quantities.∎

Q 1.26 Self-assessment question
An object of mass 0.20 kg is hung from the lower end of a spiral spring. When the object is pulled down 5.0 cm below its equilibrium position O and released, it vibrates with s.h.m. with a period of 2.0 s.
(a) What is the velocity of the mass as it passes through O?
(b) What is its acceleration when it is 2.5 cm above O?∎

Q 1.27 Self-assessment question
The dampers (shock absorbers) have been removed from a car so that it behaves like a mass supported on a spring (actually four springs). The mass of the car is 1000 kg, and when a man of mass 60 kg sits centrally, it goes down by 12 mm. Assuming that the front and back springs are equivalent and obey Hooke's law, calculate the period of vibration of the car. Criticise the assumptions made and try to work out the effect of using a simple model instead of a more complex and realistic one.∎

The simple pendulum

A simple pendulum consists of a mass attached to the end of a piece of thread. When the sphere is drawn to one side and then released the sphere will swing to and fro (figure 1.12).

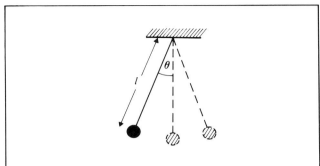

Figure 1.12 Simple pendulum

Q 1.28 Study question
Show from first principles that for small amplitudes the motion of the pendulum is simple harmonic and that its period of motion is given by

$$T = 2\pi\sqrt{\frac{l}{g}}$$

where l is the length of the pendulum.
Take particular note of the reason why it is essential to keep to small oscillations.∎

Q 1.29 Self-assessment question
Outline the energy changes that take place during one complete vibration of a simple pendulum, indicating where p.e. and k.e. have maximum and zero values.∎

Q 1.30 Self-assessment question
A simple pendulum of length 80 cm is vibrating with an amplitude of 4.0 cm. Calculate the maximum velocity of the pendulum bob.∎

Q **1.31 Study question**
Describe, with full experimental details, how you would perform an experiment, based on the expression derived in question 1.28, to measure the value of the acceleration due to gravity. Show how you would calculate the value from the experimental results.■

1.3 Energy of an oscillator

The kinetic energy of an oscillating body clearly varies during the cycle. There is a continual change of energy from kinetic energy to potential energy and *vice-versa*. At any instant during the motion the total energy of the system is equal to the sum of the kinetic energy of the moving mass and the potential energy that is stored in the system. What are the factors that determine the energy of the vibrating system? How does the energy vary with time and displacement during a cycle?

Q **1.32 Development question**
In this question you will consider the energy changes that take place in a vibrating system. Suppose that a body of mass m, which is attached to a spring, oscillates on a horizontal frictionless surface (figure 1.13).
Note: We are considering an ideal oscillator, which once started will continue for ever! We are assuming that there is no energy loss as a result of friction or other resistances to motion.

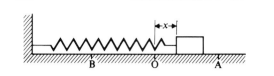

Figure 1.13 An ideal oscillator

(a) Show that the kinetic energy E_k at a displacement x is given by $\frac{1}{2} m \omega^2 (a^2 - x^2)$, where a is the amplitude of the motion.
(b) As the body moves towards A, work is done by the body on the spring. Show that the potential energy E_p at a displacement x is given by $\frac{1}{2} m \omega^2 x^2$.
(c) Show that the total energy E at displacement x (i.e. the sum of E_k and E_p) is given by

$$E = \tfrac{1}{2} m \omega^2 a^2 \quad ■$$

Q **1.33 Self-assessment question**
You should recall that, for an object moving with s.h.m., $x = a \sin \omega t$ and $\dot{x} = a \omega \cos \omega t$.
(a) Write down expressions for E_k and E_p using these formulae.
(b) Using these expressions, show that at any instant the total energy is $\frac{1}{2} m \omega^2 a^2$ (as before).■

Q **1.34 Self-assessment question**
The graph in figure 1.14 shows the variation of the potential energy of the system with displacement. Copy the diagram and draw on it graphs to show how the kinetic energy and the total energy vary with displacement.■

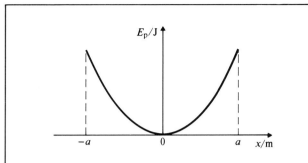

Figure 1.14 Variation of potential energy with displacement

Q **1.35 Self-assessment question**
The graph in figure 1.15 shows the variation of the kinetic energy with time during one cycle.
(a) Copy the diagram and draw on it graphs to show how the potential energy and the total energy vary with time.
(b) Why is the frequency of the energy variation twice as great as that of the vibration itself?■

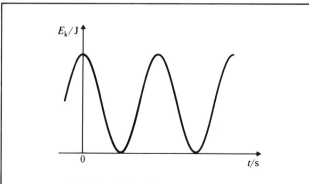

Figure 1.15 Variation of kinetic energy with time

Q 1.36 Self-assessment question
A mass of 0.50 kg is attached to a spring which has a force constant of 20 N m^{-1}. The mass is displaced a distance of 5.0 cm below the equilibrium position and then released. Calculate
(a) the maximum value of the stored potential energy,
(b) the maximum velocity of the mass,
(c) the distance from the equilibrium position when the kinetic energy is one quarter of its maximum value.■

1.4 Damped vibrations

Why do vibrations stop?

So far in this analysis of the motion of a vibrating system we have not considered the effect of forces such as those caused by friction and air resistance.

Q 1.37 Self-assessment question
Oscillations do not go on for ever, they die away and the vibrating system will eventually come to rest.
(a) What causes the amplitude of the motion to decrease?
(b) What happens to the energy of the oscillator?■

Q 1.38 Study question
Find out the precise meaning of the terms *damping* and *dissipative force* when used in the context of vibrations.■

In practice, the motion of an oscillator will depend upon the magnitude of the damping. In certain cases the damping may prevent the system from oscillating and it will just return to its equilibrium position.

Q 1.39 Self-assessment question
Give examples of a lightly-damped and of a heavily-damped system.■

How does the amplitude decrease?

E Experiment VW 2
Effect of damping on a vibrating system
The aim of this experiment is to find out how the amplitude of a vibrating system changes with time when damping forces are present.

The way in which the amplitude of the motion decays depends upon the nature of the damping forces. In experiment VW 2 the main damping force was air resistance, and you should have found out that the nature of decay did not follow the suggested mathematical pattern.

The energy lost during a swing depends upon the speed of the moving parts of the system and the distance it travels. This means that more energy will be lost during the first swing than during the second swing, and so on. The vibrations die down quickly at first and change less

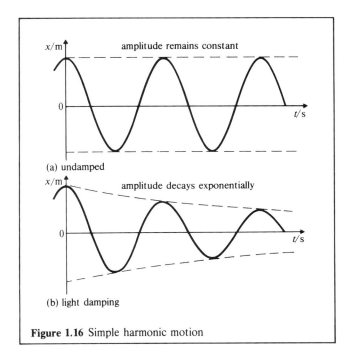

(a) undamped

(b) light damping

Figure 1.16 Simple harmonic motion

dramatically for later swings. In fact, for a damping force which is proportional to the velocity of the mass, the decay in amplitude is *exponential* (figure 1.16). This means that the amplitude decreases by the same fraction during each vibration.
Note: A full mathematical analysis of damped harmonic motion shows that the frequency of the damped motion is slightly less than the undamped frequency.■

EXTENSION

A mathematical analysis of damped s.h.m.

Suppose that the damping force opposing the motion of the mass attached to a spring (figure 1.7) is proportional to the negative of the velocity of the mass. How does this damping force affect the equation of motion?

In the *undamped* situation we have

$$T_1 - mg = -kx$$

that is

$$F = -kx$$

where F is the restoring force and k is the force constant.

The effect of the damping force F_d is to decrease the magnitude of the restoring force, that is

$$F - F_d = -kx$$

But $\quad F_d = -c\dot{x}$

where c is a positive constant determined by the magnitude of the damping. The negative sign takes account of the fact that the damping force is in the direction opposite to the velocity.

Thus $\quad m\ddot{x} = -kx - c\dot{x}$

$$m\frac{d^2x}{dt^2} = -kx - c\frac{dx}{dt}$$

This is a complicated differential equation and one form of the solution is

$$x = a\,e^{-\gamma t}\sin(\omega t + \phi)$$

Thus we have a sinusoidal motion whose amplitude $a\,e^{-\gamma t}$ decays exponentially with time, where γ is a decay constant.

Note: For light damping ω^2 is almost equal to k/m, which is the same value that it has for undamped oscillations.

Background reading

Details of the solution of the differential equation are given in Williams, Appendix 8.

Q **1.40 Study question**
Distinguish, with the aid of displacement–time graphs, between the following three categories of damping:
(a) *light damping* which results in a decreasing amplitude of vibration;
(b) *critical damping,* where the time taken for the displacement to become zero is a *minimum;*
(c) *heavy damping* where no oscillation occurs and the system returns very slowly to the equilibrium position. ■

Q **1.41 Self-assessment question**
Why are the shock absorbers of a car and instruments such as balances and electrical meters designed to produce critical damping? ■

Q **1.42 Self-assessment question**
The amplitude of the motion of a vibrating system at a certain instant of time was 4.0 cm. After an interval of time it was found to be 2.0 cm. What fraction of the energy of the system was dissipated in this time? ■

Q **1.43 Self-assessment question**
Why is it desirable for a loudspeaker to be heavily damped? ■

1.5 Forced vibrations and resonance

How can we keep the vibrations going?

Since all macroscopic mechanical oscillations are damped, energy is continually being lost from the system. If we wish to maintain the vibrations at a constant amplitude, then energy must be supplied at the rate at which energy is being dissipated in the surroundings and within the system. A force must therefore be applied to oppose the damping forces.

How must the force be applied to the system?

Is a steady or a periodic force required to maintain steady oscillations? This can be demonstrated with Barton's pendulums (figure 1.17). This consists of a number of very light pendulums (made from paper cones) of varying length and one pendulum with a heavy bob. This massive pendulum is called the driver pendulum. All the pendulums are suspended from the same string.

E **Experiment VW3**
Barton's pendulums

The aim of this experiment is to observe what happens when a system is made to vibrate at some frequency other than its own natural frequency of vibration.

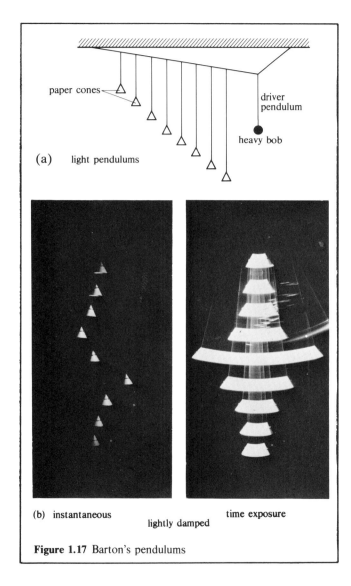

(a) light pendulums

(b) instantaneous   time exposure

lightly damped

Figure 1.17 Barton's pendulums

What are forced vibrations?

The motion of the pendulums in experiment VW 3 can be divided into two distinct sections. Initially, it is very chaotic; the pendulums tend to vibrate at their own natural frequency (determined by their length) while the driving pendulum tries to make them all vibrate at its own frequency. Gradually, the driving pendulum wins and the pendulums are all forced to vibrate at a frequency which is not the same as their own natural frequency. Energy is being transferred from the driver pendulum to the driven pendulums. This is an example of *forced vibrations*.

What is resonance?

The experiment with the pendulums showed that the forced vibrations are a maximum when the natural frequency of the driven system is equal to the frequency of the driving oscillator. This is an example of *resonance*. At resonance, maximum energy is being transferred by way of the string from the driving system to the driven system.

Another important feature that you should have observed is that when resonance occurred the two pendulums were not in phase. The displacement of the driven pendulum reached its maximum value exactly a quarter of a period after that of the driving pendulum. In other words, the phase difference is $\pi/2$ rad with the driving pendulum leading the driven pendulum.

To help you understand this, suppose that you are pushing a child on a swing. When do you give the push? When the swing is at the limit (extreme position) of its vibration. But at this point your arms must be moving with their greatest velocity (to give the maximum push), that is, they are at the centre of their to-and-fro motion. Thus, your arms are a quarter of a period ahead of the motion of the swing.

Q **1.44 Study question**
Explain what is meant by a forced vibration. Hence explain what is meant by resonance. State the conditions for resonance to occur.■

What determines the amplitude of forced vibrations?

The way in which a vibrating system responds to different driving frequencies can be investigated using a hacksaw blade oscillator.

E **Experiment VW 4**
An investigation of resonance
The aim of this experiment is to investigate what happens when a system which can vibrate at a definite frequency is driven by another vibrating system whose frequency can be varied.

Q **1.45 Study question**
The graph, figure 1.18, shows how the amplitude a of a forced vibration depends upon the driving frequency f when the damping of the system is (a) light and (b) heavy. Explain the features of these response curves, using the following words in your description: forced vibration, natural frequency, resonance and resonant frequency, amplitude and damping.■

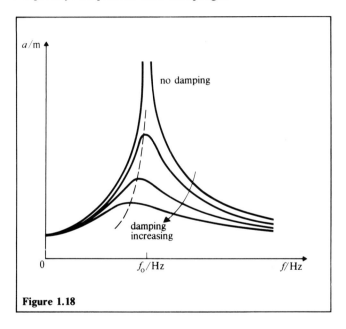

Figure 1.18

Summary
The amplitude of a forced vibration depends upon:
1 the damping of the system,
2 the relative values of the driving frequency f and the natural frequency f_0 of free vibration (i.e. how far f is from f_0).
The vibrations with largest amplitude (i.e. resonance) occur when f is approximately equal to f_0.

The effect of damping is
1 to cause the maximum amplitude to be reached when the driven frequency is less than the natural frequency,
2 to make the resonance less sharp.
Note: For most purposes, the resonant frequency can be regarded as equal to the natural frequency of the free vibration of the driven system.

The frequency of a forced vibration is the same as the frequency of the driving force but, in general, it is not in phase. At resonance the forced vibration is a quarter of a vibration behind the driver (we say that there is a phase lag of $\pi/2$ rad).

What is a coupled system?

In the pendulum experiment VW 3 the inertia of the driver pendulum was much larger than that of the driven pendulum and it was assumed that its motion was unaffected by being connected to the other vibrating pendulums. This is not the case when the oscillators have equal mass.

A pair of oscillators between which there is a connection that can transfer energy back and forth between the two is called a coupled system, e.g. two pendulums of the same length (and hence the same period) and mass joined together by means of a cord.

E **Experiment VW5**
Coupled pendulums
The aim of this experiment is to observe and explain what happens when two pendulums of equal mass are coupled together.

AV **VW1 Filmloop**
Coupled oscillators
This loop illustrates the energy transfer between two coupled pendulums.

You should have observed in experiment VW 5 and AV VW 1 how the pendulums interchanged roles. Can the terms driver and driven pendulum be used in this situation?

If a series of pendulums are coupled in this way, the energy is transferred from one to the next until the final pendulum is reached. It then returns again in the opposite direction. This process constitutes a propagation of energy and is analogous to a pulse being sent along a string. This is considered in the next chapter.

Why is resonance important?

The phenomenon of resonance is important in many areas of physics and engineering. In the next chapter you will be studying resonance in vibrating strings and air columns.

Electrical resonance will be studied in the Unit *Electromagnetism*. When you tune a radio receiver, you are making the natural frequency of the electrical oscillations equal to the frequency of the incoming radio waves.

When a beam of electromagnetic radiation, e.g. long wavelength infrared radiation, is passed through a thin film of sodium chloride, it is found that the substance absorbs energy at a particular frequency. A sodium chloride crystal contains sodium ions and chloride ions which are electrically charged. These ions can be made to oscillate by applying a varying electric field. At a certain frequency a resonant condition is set up. At this frequency a lot of the incident radiation is absorbed. From experiments like this, the chemist can find out information about the type of chemical bonding between atoms in the molecule.

Resonance is not always useful, however. At Angers in 1850, a French infantry battalion was marching over a suspension bridge when it collapsed, resulting in the deaths of 220 men. Since that time, it has been common practice to order soldiers to break step when crossing a bridge. Why do you think this happened? A more modern bridge disaster occurred in 1940 when wind-induced oscillations caused the collapse of the Tacoma Narrows Bridge (see page 4).

Engineers have to carry out elaborate vibration tests on model structures of, for example, bridges, buildings and aeroplanes before they are satisfied that the design features will prevent extremely large amplitudes being built up in the system. An excellent account of the aerodynamic problems associated with buildings and bridges is to be found in the article 'The Severn Bridge'.

In chapter 3 of this Unit you will be considering spectra, and will find out that the spectrum of light from the sun is crossed by dark lines, called Fraunhöfer lines. Particular frequencies of the sun's photosphere radiation are absorbed by gases in the chromosphere through which the light passes. This is another example of resonance.

AV **VW2 Filmloop**
Tacoma Narrows Bridge Collapse
This loop shows how wind-induced oscillations led to the collapse of the bridge.

Background reading

'The Severn Bridge', by D. E. Walshe & L. R. Wooton, in *Nuffield advanced physics: Students' book 4, Waves & oscillations.*

Q 1.46 Study question

You should do part (a) and/or part (b) of this question.

(a) Make a list of examples of resonance from different branches of physics. Make brief notes on at least three different examples.

(b) Write a brief account of resonance to explain it to somebody who has not studied science, including references to the following examples: a child on a swing, the production of musical sounds, tuning a radio receiver.∎

Questions on objectives

1 A particle moves with uniform angular velocity ω in a circular path of radius r. Show that the projection of the motion of the particle on a diameter of the circle is simple harmonic motion.

(objective 4)

2 A point mass m which is suspended by a spring of neglible mass performs simple harmonic motion of amplitude a. The graph in figure 1.19 shows the displacement with time of the mass for one complete cycle of the motion.

(a) Sketch curves to show the variation with time, for one complete cycle of the motion, of (i) the velocity of the mass, (ii) the acceleration of the mass, (iii) the force acting on the mass.

(b) Sketch a curve to show how the acceleration of the mass varies with displacement during one complete cycle of the motion.

(objective 5)

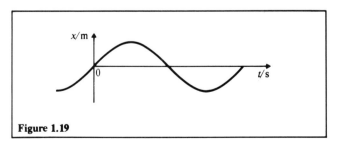

Figure 1.19

3 Show that a simple pendulum describes simple harmonic motion if its amplitude is small and derive an expression for its period of oscillation.

(objectives 3 and 6)

4 Show that the period of oscillation of a mass m which is supported by a light spring is $2\pi\sqrt{m/k}$, where k is the force constant of the spring.

(objectives 3 and 6)

5 The graph in figure 1.20 shows how the potential energy of a particle which is performing simple harmonic motion varies with the displacement of the particle from the equilibrium position. Draw graphs to show how (i) the kinetic energy of the particle, and (ii) the total energy of the particle, vary with the displacement.

(objective 7)

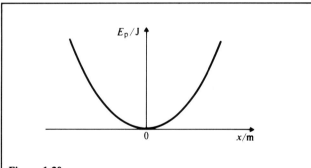

Figure 1.20

6   The displacement–time relationship for a particle which is performing simple harmonic motion can be represented by the equation

$$x = a \sin (\omega t + \phi)$$

(a) State the meaning of the symbols a and ϕ.
(b) Derive expressions for (i) the velocity of the particle at displacement x, and (ii) the maximum velocity of the particle.

(objective 8)

7   The displacement of a particle which is performing simple harmonic motion can be described by the expression

$$x = (0.05 \text{ m}) \sin 8\pi t$$

(a) What is the amplitude of the motion?
(b) What is the frequency of the motion?
(c) The particle starts its motion at time $t = 0$. How long does it take for one complete oscillation?
(d) What is the velocity of the particle (i) as it passes through its equilibrium position, and (ii) at the extreme end of the swing?
(e) What is the maximum acceleration of the particle during its motion?

(objective 9)

8   A body of mass 300 g is performing simple harmonic motion with an amplitude of 30 mm. The maximum force which acts on the body is 0.081 N. Calculate the maximum acceleration, the maximum velocity and the period of oscillation of the body.

(objective 9)

9   Discuss the effect of damping on the amplitude of a vibrating system.

(objective 10)

10   (a) Explain what is meant by resonance.
(b) Describe two examples of resonance, one in which this phenomenon is useful and the other in which it could be classed as a nuisance.

(objective 14)

Chapter 2

Aim

The aim of this chapter is to enable you to gain an understanding of the factors that determine the speed of transverse waves in strings and longitudinal waves in gases, and the ways in which progressive waves can be superimposed to form stationary waves. You will observe the behaviour of vibrating strings and resonance in an air column, perform experiments to determine the speed of sound in air, and study important applications of stationary waves.

Die Orgel in der Kirchen Zur Heil. Dreyfaltigkeit in Ulm.

Objectives

When you have completed the work in this chapter you should be able to:

1 Use the following scientific terms correctly: stationary (standing) wave, node, antinode, fundamental, harmonic, overtone, quality, resonance tube, end-correction.

2 Explain, with the aid of models such as springs and coupled dynamics trolleys, the factors affecting (i) the speed of transverse waves in strings and wires, (ii) the speed of longitudinal waves in a medium.

3 Describe and explain, with the aid of diagrams and appropriate experiments, the formation of stationary (standing) waves.

4 Recall and use the fact that the distance between consecutive nodes and consecutive antinodes is $\lambda/2$.

5 List the differences between progressive waves and stationary waves.

6 (a) Explain how a change in temperature affects the speed of sound in a gas.
(b) Explain why the speed of sound in a gas is independent of the pressure of the gas.

7 Discuss the factors that affect the modes of vibration of vibrating strings.

8 Explain, with the aid of diagrams, the stationary wave patterns in closed and open tubes. Distinguish between displacement nodes, pressure nodes, displacement antinodes and pressure antinodes.

9 Perform and describe an experiment to determine the speed of sound in an air column (resonance tube method).

10 Solve problems involving
(a) the equations for the speed of transverse waves

$$c = \sqrt{\frac{T}{\mu}} \text{ and } c = \sqrt{\frac{\gamma p}{\rho}} = \sqrt{\frac{\gamma RT}{M_m}}$$

(b) vibrating strings and the use of the relationship

$$f = \frac{n}{2l}\sqrt{\frac{T}{\mu}}$$

(c) vibrating air columns in open and closed pipes.

11 EXTENSION
Use the equation, $y = a \sin(\omega t \pm k x)$, for a progressive wave to derive an equation for a stationary wave and explain its significance.

12 EXTENSION
Discuss the construction of stringed and wind instruments, with reference to the physical principles involved.

Experiments in chapter 2

VW 6 A study of a wave model
(1 hour)
VW 7 Stationary waves on a string
(1 hour)
VW 8 Stationary waves in an air column
(¾ hour)
VW 9 Stationary sound waves
(¾ hour)
VW 10 Vibrations in an air column
(1 hour)

References

Akrill	Chapters 16, 17, 18
Duncan FWA	Chapters 6, 7
Nelkon	Chapters 24, 29, 30
Millar	Chapters 23, 24
Wenham	Chapters 21, 23
Whelan	Chapters 12, 14, 41

Study time: 2 weeks

2.1 Speed of waves

In the Unit *Wave properties* you measured the speed of sound in air and the speed of waves along springs, and discussed the factors which affected the speed of propagation. Now we will obtain general equations for the speed of transverse waves in a string (or wire) and of longitudinal waves in an elastic medium.

We can begin by recalling a number of facts about the movement of wave pulses (you made a number of observations on wave pulses in experiment WP 1).

Q 2.1 Self-assessment question
(a) Does the speed of a pulse, in a rope or slinky, depend on the shape of the pulse (for example, its height or length)?
(b) Does the speed depend on the tension in the rope or slinky?
(c) Does the speed depend on the mass or thickness of a rope?
(d) Does friction affect the shape or speed of the pulse?
(e) Can one pulse catch up with another and pass it? ∎

We can obtain more information about the factors which affect the way a wave travels through an elastic medium by observing how a pulse travels along a line of trolleys joined by springs.

Transverse waves

E Experiment VW 6
A study of a wave model
In this experiment a wave pulse is sent through a line of trolleys joined together by springs. You will observe that the pulse speed depends upon the mass of the trolleys and the tension in the connecting springs.

In experiment VW 6 you should have found that doubling the tension increases the pulse speed and that doubling the mass of each trolley reduces it. When the mass and the tension are both doubled, the wave speed is restored to its original value, since both quantities change the speed by the same factor.

Q 2.2 Self-assessment question
Explain why (i) increase in tension, and (ii) increase in mass have opposite effects on the wave speed. ∎

We will now consider the mechanism by which a pulse travels along a string (or spring), and how one part of the string affects the next part. Figure 2.1a shows the positions of a wave pulse travelling along a string at two successive intervals of time. The solid line represents the position of the pulse at time t, and the broken line represents its position at time $(t +\Delta t)$. In the time interval Δt, point A on the string has moved to B and the leading edge of the pulse has moved along the string from A to A_1.

Q 2.3 Development question
Figure 2.1b shows the forces acting on the leading edge A of the pulse. T_1 and T are the tensions on each side of A.

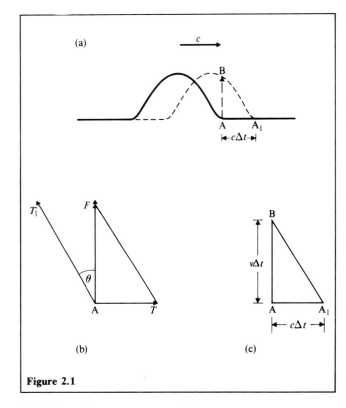

Figure 2.1

(a) Why is T_1 greater than T?
(b) Show that $T = T_1 \sin \theta$.
(c) Consider a small part of the string, of mass per unit length μ, which includes the leading edge A. A is accelerated from rest by the resultant force F and its average velocity during the time Δt is v, in the direction AB. Show that the resultant force F is given by

$$F = T_1 \cos \quad = \frac{T}{\tan \theta}$$

(d) The leading edge A moves to A_1 in time Δt, as shown in figure 2.1c. Show that the mass of string that moves in the direction AB in time Δt is $\mu c \, \Delta t$, where c is the speed of the pulse along the string.

(e) Write down an expression for the rate of change of momentum of the string, $\Delta p / \Delta t$, and hence show from Newton's second law that $F = \mu c v$.

(f) With reference to figure 2.1c, show that

$$\tan \theta = \frac{c}{v}$$

(g) By rearranging the terms in the expressions derived in parts (c), (e) and (f), show that the speed of a transverse wave along a string is given by

➤ $$c = \sqrt{\frac{T}{\mu}}$$

where T is the tension in the undisplaced part of the string.■

Notes: 1 You will not be expected to recall this proof in an examination.
2 The argument also applies to a periodic wave, which is just a series of pulses following one another.
3 This relationship can be verified experimentally using the trolley and spring model. But must be the mass per unit length of the *system* (not the mass per unit length of the *springs*).

Q 2.4 Self-assessment question
(a) Use the method of dimensional analysis to verify the relationship between c, T and μ derived in question 2.3.
(*Hint:* assume that the relationship can be written in the form $c = k \, T^x \mu^y$, where x and y are numbers and k is a dimensionless constant.)
(b) A whip tapers towards the end. What happens to the speed of a pulse as it passes down the whip from the handle? Explain.■

Q 2.5 Self-assessment question
(a) A string of length 20 m has a mass of 100 g, and is under a tension of 10 N. What will be the speed of a pulse along it? How long will it take the pulse to travel the length of the string?
(b) Transverse waves travel at a speed of 40 m s^{-1} along a steel wire which is under a tension of 13.5 N. If the density of steel is 7.8×10^3 kg m^{-3}, what is the cross-sectional area of the wire?■

Longitudinal waves

If you did not complete the second part of experiment VW 6, now is the time to study how springiness and mass affect the speed of the longitudinal pulse in the trolleys and springs model.

Consider a section PQ in an elastic medium (e.g. air or a spring) in which a compression pulse is travelling to the right, as shown in figure 2.2. Normally there is no resultant force acting on the particles of the medium, but when a compression pulse comes along there is a resultant force, because some parts of the material are more

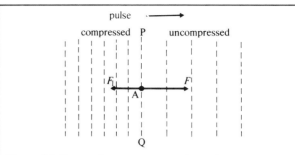

Figure 2.2 Forces due to a compression pulse on a particle in an elastic medium

compressed than others. The speed of the pulse through the material will depend on the way in which the particles in section PQ are displaced from their equilibrium position by the action of the resultant force. If the particles accelerate rapidly when the pulse reaches them, then the pulse speed will be large. The speed of the pulse depends on two factors, the inertia of the material and the elasticity of the material.

The expression for the speed of a mechanical wave in an elastic medium is of the form

$$\text{wave speed} = \sqrt{\frac{\text{elastic property}}{\text{inertial property}}}$$

Q 2.6 Study question
(a) What are the elastic and inertial properties for a longitudinal wave travelling through (i) a solid rod or bar, and (ii) a fluid?
(b) Write down the appropriate equations for the speed of a longitudinal wave through (i) a rod, and (ii) a liquid.■

Q **2.7 Self-assessment question**
(a) Calculate the speed of sound through an aluminium rod. (For aluminium, $\rho = 2.7 \times 10^3$ kg m^{-3} $E = 7.0 \times 10^{10}$ N m^{-2} (Pa).)
(b) The speed of sound in aluminium is nearly the same as its speed in steel, but the density of steel is approximately three times that of aluminium. What can you say about the Young moduli of the two metals?
(c) If sound travels at a speed of 1.45×10^3 m s^{-1} through sea water, calculate the bulk modulus for sea water. (For sea water, $\rho = 1.02 \times 10^3$ kg m^{-3}.)■

EXTENSION

Q **2.8 Development question***
Let us consider a compression pulse travelling along a bar. Figure 2.3 shows the bar being compressed at the end.
(a) After a time Δt the compression pulse, of speed c, has travelled a distance x along the bar and reached the point Q. Write down an equation for c in terms of x and Δt.
(b) As the pulse travels along the bar all parts of the bar between P and Q are moving to the right. The end P has moved to P$_1$, a distance Δx in time Δt, but the parts of the bar at Q are only just beginning to move. What is the *average* speed v of the compressed section of the bar caused by the compression?
(c) If the density of the bar is ρ and its cross-sectional area is A, what is the mass of material between P and Q that is on the move?

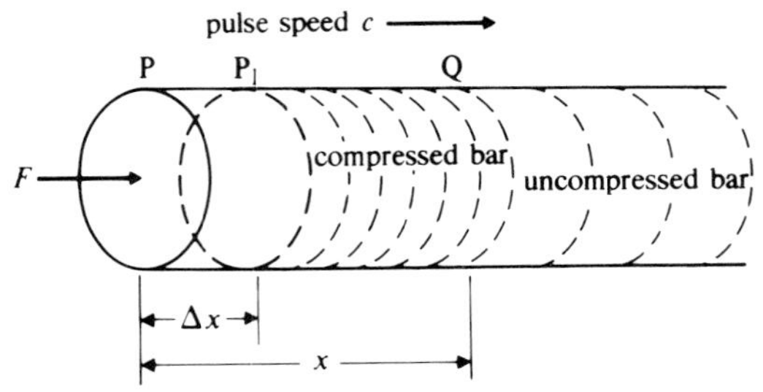

(d) What is the total change in momentum of this mass in time Δt?
(e) The change in momentum is caused by a force acting for a time Δt. The force applied to compress the bar increases steadily from 0 to F as the bar is compressed, and so the average force acting during the time Δt is $F/2$. Show that

$$F = \frac{\rho A\, x\, \Delta x}{\Delta t^2}$$

(f) After a time Δt the compression force has become F and has compressed a section of the bar of length x by an amount Δx. If E is the Young modulus for the material, write down an expression for F in terms of E.
(g) Use the equations you have deduced in parts (a), (e) and (f) to show that

$$c = \sqrt{\frac{E}{\rho}}\ ■$$

Figure 2.3 Movement of a compression pulse along a bar

Speed of sound in a gas

For sound waves in a gas, the elastic property is the pressure p of the gas and the inertial property its density ρ. It can be shown that the speed of sound waves in a gas is given by

$$\blacktriangleright \quad c = \sqrt{\frac{\gamma p}{\rho}}$$

where γ is the ratio of the principal specific or molar heat capacities of a gas (see the Unit *Thermal properties*).

Note: It can be shown that the isothermal bulk modulus of a gas is equal to its pressure p and that the adiabatic bulk modulus is equal to γp. The latter value is used because, in the audible range, sound waves travel under adiabatic conditions. We suppose that the pressure changes take place so rapidly that there is insufficient time for heat to enter or leave the gas (however, the full explanation is more complex).

Q 2.9 Self-assessment question

Use the method of dimensional analysis to show that the equation for the speed of sound in a gas is dimensionally correct. ∎

Q 2.10 Study question

(a) Use the ideal gas equation $pV_m = RT$ to show that

$$c = \sqrt{\frac{\gamma RT}{M_m}}$$

where T is the thermodynamic temperature, R is the molar gas constant and M_m is the molar mass of the gas.

(b) How does the speed of sound depend upon (i) the temperature and (ii) the nature of the gas?

(c) Explain why the speed of sound is independent of pressure for a given temperature. ∎

Q 2.11 Self-assessment question

(a) What will be the percentage change in the speed of sound waves in air caused by a 10% change in the absolute temperature of the air?

(b) What will be the change in the speed of sound waves in air caused by a 10% change in atmospheric pressure? ∎

Background reading

Bores, breakers, waves and wakes, by R.A.R Tricker, Mills and Boon, 1973 (out of print), provides a comprehensive treatment of waves on water.

Summary of wave speed formulae

Transverse waves on a string or spring (tension T, mass per unit length μ)

$$c = \sqrt{\frac{T}{\mu}}$$

Longitudinal waves in solid rods (Young modulus E, density ρ)

$$c = \sqrt{\frac{E}{\rho}}$$

Longitudinal waves in a liquid (bulk modulus K, density ρ)

$$c = \sqrt{\frac{K}{\rho}}$$

Sound waves in a gas (pressure p, density ρ, ratio of principal molar heat capacities γ, thermodynamic temperature T, molar mass M_m, molar gas constant R)

$$c = \sqrt{\frac{\gamma p}{\rho}} = \sqrt{\frac{\gamma RT}{M_m}}$$

2.2 Stationary waves

We have seen that when waves are sent down a rope, which is fixed at one end, the waves will be reflected. For certain frequencies the incident and reflected waves produce patterns, such as those illustrated in figure 2.4. In this section we will consider how this type of wave, called a *stationary* (or standing) wave, is produced.

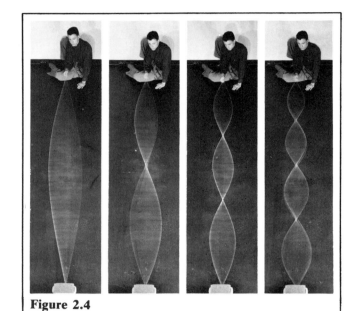

Figure 2.4

Transverse stationary waves are produced in the strings, and longitudinal stationary waves in the air columns, of musical instruments. Stationary waves, due to oscillating electrons, occur in radio and television aerial systems tuned to incoming radio waves. Electrons have wave properties. The fact that an atom has definite energy levels can be accounted for by assuming that the electron in the atom behaves like a stationary wave (see the Unit *Electrons and the nucleus*).

E Experiment VW 7
Stationary waves on a string

In this experiment you will produce a stationary wave pattern on a string and investigate the effect of changing the driving frequency and the tension in the string.

Formation of a stationary wave

The stationary wave pattern set up in experiment VW 7 was the result of the *superposition* of a wave travelling out from the vibrator and a wave reflected back at a rigid boundary along the string in the opposite direction. The pattern is the result of the superposition of two waves of *equal frequency and amplitude* travelling along the *same line* with the *same speed* but in *opposite directions*.

AV VW 3 Large transparencies
Constructing a stationary wave

An exercise designed to enable you to understand how a stationary wave is formed.

Q 2.12 Development question*

Figure 2.5 shows the displacement–distance graphs of two sinusoidal waves, R and L, of the same amplitude and frequency. R (shown by the thin line) is travelling to the right at 0.5 m s^{-1} and L (shown by the broken line) is travelling to the left at the same speed. The thick line shows the resultant wave shape, at the instant shown ($t = 0$), formed by superposition. The amplitude of each wave is 0.5 m and the wavelength 2.0 m.

(a) Copy these graphs on a sheet of graph paper.

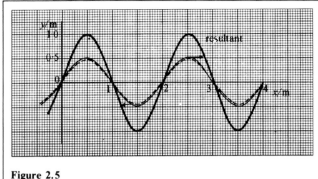

Figure 2.5

(b) Underneath your diagram draw graphs to show the positions of R and L after a time interval of 1.0 s and their resultant at this instant.

(c) Repeat (b) to show the situations when $t = 2.0$ s and when $t = 3.0$ s.

(d) Now draw the situations at $t = 0.5$ s and $t = 2.5$ s.

(e) On a single diagram, show the resultant wave shapes that you obtained in (b), (c) and (d). Your diagram will show some of the shapes taken by the resultant wave in this time interval.

(f) Which points in the medium appear to have (i) zero displacement and (ii) maximum displacement during this interval of time?

(g) What is the distance between these positions?

(h) How does this distance compare with the wavelength of the progressive waves?∎

Nodes and antinodes

The important result of this type of superposition is that the waves produced do not move through the medium (e.g. string), as shown in figure 2.6. There are points on

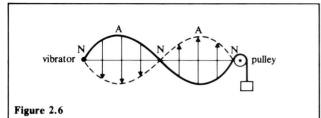

Figure 2.6

the string which have zero displacement. Such points are called *nodes*, N, and are separated by a distance of $\lambda/2$, where λ is the common wavelength of the waves. Also there are points which have maximum displacement, called *antinodes*, A. These are also separated by a distance $\lambda/2$.

Q 2.13 Self-assessment question
(a) Draw graphs to show how the displacement of a particle at (i) a nodal point and (ii) an antinodal point varies with time.
(b) How do the particles in the medium between adjacent nodes move? Comment on their phase relationships and amplitudes.
(c) How does the movement of a particle on one side of a node differ from that of a particle on the other side? ■

Q 2.14 Study question
(a) Make a summary of the differences between progressive waves and stationary waves. You should comment on the following features: (i) amplitude, (ii) frequency, (iii) wavelength, (iv) phase, (v) waveform, (vi) energy.
(b) Make brief notes on experiments to illustrate the differences between (i) transverse waves and longitudinal waves, and (ii) progressive waves and stationary waves. ■

EXTENSION

The equation of a stationary wave

To find the equation of a stationary wave, we take the equations of two progressive waves of the same frequency and amplitude travelling in opposite directions and add the disturbances together. This is the mathematical application of the principle of superposition.

The equation of a progressive wave travelling to the right is given by

$$y_1 = a \sin(\omega t - kx)$$

where ω is determined by the frequency of the wave and kx indicates the variation of y at any instant with displacement from the source. The equation of a similar wave travelling to the left is

$$y_2 = a \sin(\omega t + kx)$$

The equation of a stationary wave is the sum of these equations and therefore its displacement y will be given by

$$y = y_1 + y_2 = a \sin(\omega t - kx) + a \sin(\omega t + kx)$$

Q 2.15 Development question
Using the trigonometrical relationship

$$\sin A + \sin B = 2 \sin \left(\frac{A+B}{2}\right) \cos \left(\frac{A-B}{2}\right)$$

show that $y = 2a \cos kx \sin \omega t$ ■

Note: $\sin \omega t$ does not vary with x and $\cos kx$ does not vary with t. Thus our equation for a stationary wave is

$$y = 2a \times \text{location-dependent} \times \text{time-dependent}$$
$$\text{factor} \qquad\qquad \text{factor}$$

Q 2.16 Self-assessment question
Write equations for the variation of (i) the displacement with time at an antinode, (ii) the amplitude with location between two consecutive antinodes. ■

Stationary waves in a string

We will now consider why a stationary wave pattern in a string of fixed length only occurs at certain frequencies. When a single pulse is reflected at a rigid boundary, it is reflected upside down—a pulse in the form of a crest is reflected as a trough and *vice versa* (see the Unit *Wave properties*). We say that there is a phase change of π rad or half a cycle. When a progressive or travelling wave runs along the string, the wave is reflected at the rigid boundary and the two sets of waves combine to form a stationary wave in the string. Figure 2.7 illustrates what happens at the rigid boundary. At time $t = 0$ the wave is just arriving at the boundary.

Now let us consider what happens when the reflected wave gets back to the other end of the string. In this case we are considering it as fixed (e.g., rope held by hand or string passing over pulley). This constitutes a boundary: reflection will take place and the wave will travel back down the string. The reflected wave will combine with new waves being fed in from the source. If it is in step with these waves, they will reinforce each other and build up a wave of larger amplitude. If it is not in step, they will partially or completely cancel each other out, depending on the phase relation between the two sets of waves.

The frequency of the source can be changed, as in experiment VW 7, until a stationary wave pattern is formed at a particular frequency f. The time taken for the wave to travel along the string depends upon the wave speed c (which is determined by the tension and the mass per unit length) and the distance l between the two fixed ends. Because there are two phase changes, the reflected

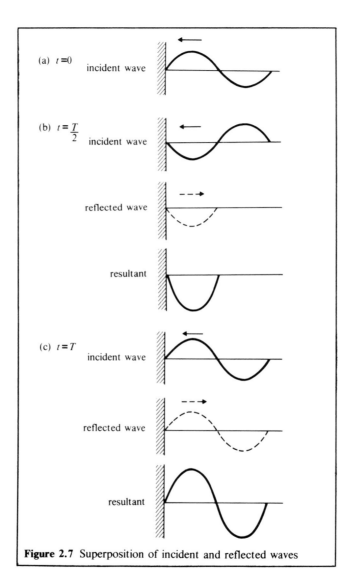

Figure 2.7 Superposition of incident and reflected waves

wave will be in phase with the new waves if the time taken to travel twice the length of the string is nT, where T is the periodic time. Therefore

$$l = \frac{cnT}{2} = \frac{n\lambda}{2}$$

As the frequency of the source approaches the natural frequency of the string, stationary waves are formed. When the frequencies exactly coincide, the amplitude of the stationary waves will be maximum—this is called *resonance*.

Alternatively, if the source frequency cannot be adjusted, stationary wave patterns can be produced by changing the natural frequency of the string (for example, by changing l or T).

Q 2.17 Self-assessment question
A string is fixed at both ends. Trace the passage of a progressive wave, starting at one end, along the cord and explain how a stationary wave pattern of large amplitude, as in figure 2.8, is produced.■

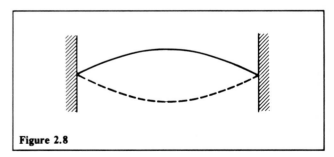

Figure 2.8

Q 2.18 Self-assessment question

(a) Show that for a string of length l, which is fixed at both ends,

$$f = n \frac{c}{2l}$$

where f is the natural frequency of the string and n is a whole number.

(b) Explain what happens for values of $f \neq n \, (c/2l)$. To what type of vibration is the string being subjected?

(c) Explain why, in practice, (i) there is not zero displacement at the nodes and (ii) it is possible to obtain a stationary wave pattern even if f is not an integral multiple of $c/2l$. ∎

Q 2.19 Self-assessment question

A vibrator is driven from the a.c. mains at a frequency of 50 Hz and has a string under a tension of 4.9 N attached to it. The other end of the string is fixed (but adjustable). The mass per unit length of the string is $1.0 \times 10^{-3} \ \mathrm{kg \ m^{-1}}$.

(a) What is the speed of a transverse wave along the string?

(b) Calculate the length of string which will show a stationary wave pattern with three antinodes. ∎

Stationary waves in air

Stationary waves can be obtained in air by using a tube which is either closed or open at one end. The air at the other end is vibrated by means of a loudspeaker which is electrically driven by a signal generator. Progressive longitudinal waves travel down the tube, are reflected, and superimpose with the incident wave to give rise to a longitudinal stationary wave. The apparatus is some- times referred to as Kundt's tube (although he did not use a signal generator—his source of longitudinal waves was a vibrating rod).

AV VW 4 Filmloop
Standing sound waves

This loop shows the formation of stationary waves in air and in a spiral spring.

E Experiment VW 8
Stationary waves in an air column

To investigate how the air vibrates in a tube and measure the speed of sound in an air column.

In experiment VW 8, the stationary wave is detected by placing a small quantity of lycopodium powder (the pollen of a particular fern) in the tube. You should have observed that the powder gathered into piles at different locations along the tube. These points are nodes—points of zero particle displacement.

Q 2.20 Self-asessment question

In a dust-tube experiment to measure the speed of sound in carbon dioxide at a temperature of 289 K, one end of the tube was closed and the other end fitted to a loudspeaker connected to a signal generator. At a frequency of 850 Hz resonance occurred, and the nodes were separated by a mean distance of 0.16 m. Use this information to calculate the speed of sound in carbon dioxide at 273 K. ∎

In between the nodes, the amplitude of the imposed particle vibration varies with location. The following exercise will help you to visualise a longitudinal stationary wave.

1 Cut a slit 2 mm wide and 90 mm long in a 100 mm × 150 mm card (or fasten two cards edge-to-edge with a 2 mm gap).

2 Place the card over figure 2.9 with the slit at the top of the diagram.

3 Move the card downward with a constant velocity. The parts of the curves which appear in the slit correspond to the vibrations of the particles in a longitudinal stationary wave.

Figure 2.9

A stationary wave set up in an air column exists as both a stationary wave of particle displacement and as a stationary wave of pressure variation. When a stationary sound wave is illustrated, it is important to distinguish between these two sets of waves.

Q 2.21 Self-assessment question

What can you say about the pressure at (i) a point where the particles are crowded together, and (ii) a point where the particles are removed in both directions?■

Figure 2.10 illustrates the variation of longitudinal particle displacement with location at two instants of time, t and $(t + T/2)$. The length of the arrow indicates the amplitude of the particle displacement and the direction shown is for time t.

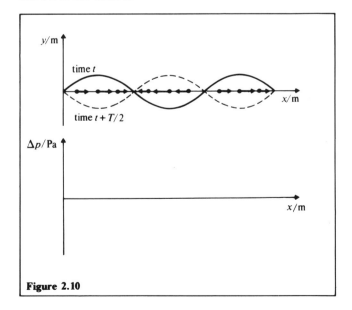

Figure 2.10

Q 2.22 Self-assessment question

Copy figure 2.10. Using the same scale for the x-axis, draw graphs to illustrate the pressure variation at these two instants of time.■

The pressure variation is always a maximum at a displacement node and is always zero at a displacement antinode. In the next experiment, a microphone is used to locate the positions of maximum and zero pressure variation in a stationary wave in free air.

E Experiment VW 9
Stationary sound waves

In this experiment you will investigate the formation of a stationary wave pattern in air and measure the speed of sound in free air.

Background reading

Waves and the ear, by W. A. Van Bergeijk, J. R. Pierce, and E. E. David, Jr., Heinemann (Science study series), 1961, (out of print).

Comprehension exercise

Striking evidence for the wave nature of electromagnetic radiation can occasionally be noted by motorway drivers with car radios. The following true account is an example.

Observation

Driving on the M4 from Bristol to London at a steady 65 miles per hour (29 m s^{-1}). Radio tuned to BBC Radio 2 (wavelength 330 metres). Very noticeable and regular cyclic variation of volume from radio. Interval, as roughly timed with a wristwatch over a number of cycles: approximately 6 seconds. Volume variation most marked in the region of motorway junction 16 (figure 2.11).

Facts

1 Two transmitters operating at 330 metres: Clevedon near Bristol (medium power) and Brookmans Park near London (high power).
2 Received intensities approximately equal in the region of junction 16.
3 Motorway runs in almost direct line between the two transmitters.

Interpretation

A superposition effect; with 330 metres broadcast the stationary wave pattern repeats every 165 metres. Time interval between successive maxima approximately $5\frac{3}{4}$ seconds.

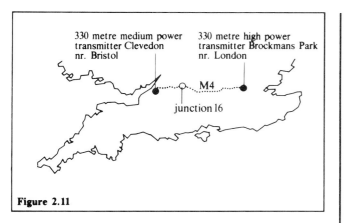

Figure 2.11

Questions

1 Why is this evidence that radio transmissions have a wave nature?

2 What would you hear on the radio of a car as you drove along the M4 near Junction 16 listening to the radio? Write your answer as if explaining to a non-scientist what he would hear.

3 Explain, again as if to a non-scientist, why the amplitude and hence the intensity of the radio signal rises and falls.

4 Is it the audio modulation of the radio waves or the radio waves themselves that are superimposed to produce the stationary wave pattern?

2.3 Vibrations in strings

The vibrating string, struck, plucked or bowed, forms the basis of probably the most important class of musical instruments. In this section we will be concerned with the factors that determine the frequency and quality of the note produced by a vibrating string.

When a string vibrates, progressive transverse waves travel along the string to both ends, which are fixed, where they are reflected and combine with the incident waves. A stationary wave pattern is formed for waves whose wavelengths are correctly matched to the length of the string and the sound produced is transmitted to the surrounding air.

Q **2.23 Self-assessment question**
How is the intensity of a note produced by a string in a musical instrument increased (without the aid of electrical amplifiers)?∎

Modes of vibration

The simplest mode of vibration of a string occurs when it is plucked at the centre and there is an antinode between the fixed ends (nodes) of the string, as shown in figure 2.12a.

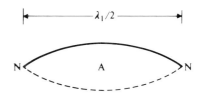

(a) fundamental or first harmonic, frequency f_1

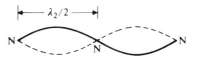

(b) first overtone or second harmonic, frequency f_2

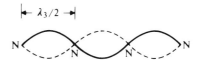

(c) second overtone or third harmonic, frequency f_3

(d) third overtone or fourth harmonic, frequency f_4

Figure 2.12 Modes of vibration of a string

Q 2.24 Development question
(a) The length of the string is l, the tension in the string is T and its mass per unit length is μ. Show that the frequency of the fundamental note is given by

$$\rightarrow \quad f_1 = \frac{1}{2l}\sqrt{\frac{T}{\mu}}$$

(b) When the string is plucked at a point which is a quarter of the string's length from one end, it vibrates as shown in figure 2.12b. Show that the frequency f_2 of the note is given by $f_2 = 2f_1$.
(c) Figures 2.12c and 2.12d show other possible modes of vibration. Write down a general expression for the frequencies produced.■

Q 2.25 Self-assessment question
A wire is tuned to vibrate at a frequency of 1 kHz. What will the fundamental frequency of vibration be if
(a) its tension is doubled (assume length and mass per unit length unchanged),
(b) its length is doubled (assume tension is still doubled and mass per unit length unchanged),
(c) its mass per unit length is doubled (assuming tension and length are still doubled)?■

Laws of a vibrating string
From the above discussion, it follows that

$$f_1 \propto \frac{1}{2l}, \text{ if } T \text{ and } \mu \text{ are constant}$$

$$f_1 \propto T^{\frac{1}{2}}, \text{ if } l \text{ and } \mu \text{ are constant}$$

$$f_1 \propto \mu^{-\frac{1}{2}}, \text{ if } T \text{ and } l \text{ are constant}$$

These three statements are known as the laws of vibration of stretched strings or Mersenne's laws (published by him in 1636). They can be verified experimentally using a sonometer, or by the arrangement used in experiment VW 7 (Melde's experiment).

Q 2.26 Study question
Make brief notes on how you would verify experimentally the relationship between the frequency of the fundamental note emitted by a stretched wire and (i) its tension, (ii) its length, (iii) its mass per unit length. You should include details of the experimental procedure, the results you would record and the graphs that you would plot.■

Q 2.27 Self-assessment question
(a) How does the frequency of a wire of given material and given length under a fixed tension depend upon its diameter?
(b) A stretched steel wire of diameter 5.0×10^{-4} m is supported at two points 0.30 m apart. Calculate the tension that must be applied to make its fundamental frequency 500 Hz.
(Density of steel = 7.8×10^3 kg m^{-3}.)■

Q 2.28 Self-assessment question
A copper wire is stretched horizontally so that its centre is between the poles of two strong magnets. The distance between the supports is 0.75 m and the mass per unit length of the wire is 1.8×10^{-3} kg m^{-1}. The wire carries an alternating current of frequency 50 Hz.
(a) The current is switched on and the tension in the wire is adjusted until a position is reached when the wire is seen to be vibrating in one loop with large amplitude. Explain why this happens.
(b) Calculate the tension in the wire.■

Quality of a musical note
It is not difficult to distinguish notes of the same pitch played on different instruments. Analysis of such notes shows that the quality of the sound heard depends on the shape of the waveform of the vibrations reaching the listener. Several factors affect this waveform.

When a guitar string is plucked, the stationary wave produced in the string does not have a simple sine wave shape. The waveform has a pointed shape at first and changes its shape as the vibrations die away. Any regularly repeated wave pattern, however complex, can be built up by adding together a series of sine waves with frequencies which are all multiples of a fundamental frequency. Figure 2.13 shows how a complex waveform is produced by adding together sine waves of frequencies f, $2f$ and $3f$.

The frequencies which are integral multiples of the fundamental are called *harmonics*. The particular shape of the wave depends on which harmonics are present and their relative intensities. The vibrating guitar string produces a complex vibration which includes the fundamental and a whole series of harmonics and the particular waveform can by changed by plucking at a different place or in a different way. These many frequencies produced by the string act as forcing vibrations to produce resonant vibrations of the wood of the guitar body and the air inside it. All frequencies higher than the fundamental are called overtones. Some may definitely not be harmonics, like the high-pitched squeals produced by a bad violin player which are caused by inharmonic torsional oscillations of the string.

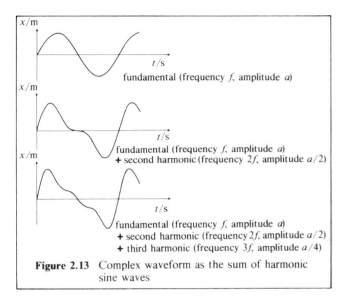

Figure 2.13 Complex waveform as the sum of harmonic sine waves

AV VW 5 Slideset and audio tape Musical notes

As you view the slides and listen to the recording, you will discover how the quality of a note depends on the design of the instrument, the way it is played and even the room it is played in.

Q 2.29 Self-assessment question
(a) Explain the term quality and state the physical properties of sound waves on which it depends.
(b) What is meant by the fundamental frequency? Distinguish between harmonics and overtones.■

EXTENSION

Q 2.30 Study question
(a) Why is a violin box shaped the way it is?
(b) How can a violinist change the quality of the note produced by his instrument?
(c) In what other shapes are sound boxes made? Suggest how they affect the sound produced.■

Pitch

A sound is said to have a pitch if it has associated with it a distinct recognisable musical note or tone. Pitch is the musical term describing what we hear, while frequency is a scientific term describing what we can measure. A certain pitch corresponds directly to a certain fundamental frequency. (On the other hand, a noise is a sound which has no identifiable pitch.)

The most important interval of pitch is an octave—the interval between two notes whose frequencies are in the ratio 1:2. The octave can be subdivided into a scale of notes. Different cultures and ages have evolved different scales—the one we are familiar with is the diatonic scale represented in table 2.1. This is a scale of notes which can begin on any frequency and proceed, by the intervals shown, to the octave above. In music, the term interval represents a frequency *ratio*.

Table 2.1

		C	D	E	F	G	A	B	C
Note		doh	re	me	fah	soh	lah	te	doh
Frequency		256							
Frequency ratio of adjacent notes			$\frac{9}{8}$	$\frac{10}{9}$	$\frac{16}{15}$	$\frac{9}{8}$	$\frac{10}{9}$	$\frac{9}{8}$	$\frac{16}{15}$

Q 2.31 Self-assessment question
Complete the line in table 2.1 giving the frequencies.■

Q 2.32 Self-assessment question
How is it possible to play a scale on a guitar or violin using
(a) only one string,
(b) two or more strings?■

EXTENSION

Q 2.33 Study question
You will have noticed in table 2.1 that musicians do not seem to divide an octave into equal units to produce a scale. Justify this practice, against the desire for a more logical approach of dividing it into eight equal steps. (If you want to pursue this further, find out about the even-temperament scale and its advantages and disadvantages.)■

2.4 Vibrations in air columns

The vibrating column of air in a tube or pipe is the basis of many forms of musical instrument. In this section we will study the formation of stationary waves in closed and open pipes and discuss the different modes of vibration.

The air can be set vibrating in many ways: for example, by blowing air over an edge or by means of a vibrating reed. Longitudinal progressive waves travel from the source of disturbance, are reflected back from the other end of the pipe and superimpose with incident waves to form a longitudinal stationary wave. Resonance will occur only for those wavelengths that fit the length of the pipe.

Q 2.34 Self-assessment question

(a) If you blow across the mouth of a milk bottle or boiling tube which is partially filled with water, a note is produced. Does the pitch of this note depend upon (i) how hard you blow, (ii) the depth of the water in the tube?

(b) What happens to the pitch of the note produced by blowing over the end of an open cardboard tube when you close the other end with your hand.

(If you do not know the answers, try out these simple experiments.)■

We will now consider the factors that determine the lowest frequency (i.e. the fundamental mode of vibration) produced by a closed pipe (that is, one that is closed at one end) and an open pipe (that is, one that is open at both ends).

Q 2.35 Development question

Consider compression pulses travelling down a closed tube and an open tube.

(a) How will the pulse be reflected at (i) the closed end, (ii) the open end?

(b) When the pulses arrive back at the other end, how will they be reflected?

(c) For resonance to occur, what can you say about the phase relationship between the incident pulse from the source and the reflected pulse?

(d) What can you say about the displacement amplitude at (i) the closed end, (ii) the open end?

(e) What can you say about the excess pressure amplitude at (i) the closed end, (ii) the open end?

(f) Draw diagrams to illustrate the longitudinal stationary wave particle displacement for the first position of resonance in (i) the closed tube, (ii) the open tube.

(g) Derive expressions for the fundamental frequency of (i) the closed tube, (ii) the open tube, in terms of the length l of the tube and the speed of sound c. (Assume that the position of the displacement antinode coincides with the end of the tube.)

(h) Hence show that the fundamental frequency of the open pipe is twice that of a closed pipe of the same length.■

Q 2.36 Study question

(a) Explain why the effective length of the vibrating air column exceeds the length of the pipe.

(b) What is meant by the end-correction? How is it related to the radius of the pipe?■

Modes of vibration

E Experiment VW 10 Vibrations in an air column

To study the resonant vibrations in an air column and measure the speed of sound.

When a closed tube of fixed length is energised, with progressive waves of various frequencies, it resonates to frequencies equal to f_0, $3f_0$, $5f_0$, etc. That is, it resonates to a fundamental and all the *odd* harmonics, but not the even harmonics. An open tube resonates to frequencies equal to f_0, $2f_0$, $3f_0$, etc. (i.e. to a fundamental and *all* the harmonics).

Note: For closed and open pipes of equal length, the fundamental frequencies are not the same.

Q 2.37 Study question
(a) Draw diagrams to show the position of the displacement nodes and displacement antinodes in two organ pipes of the same length, one with a closed end and the other with an open end, when they are sounding (i) the fundamental frequency, (ii) the first overtone, (iii) the second overtone.
(b) Show, neglecting end-corrections, that (i) for the closed pipe, the overtone frequency f_n is given by

$$f_n = (2n + 1) f_0$$

where f_0 is the fundamental frequency of the closed pipe and $n = 1, 2, 3, \ldots$, and (ii) for the open pipe, the overtone frequency $f_n{}^1$ is

$$f_n{}^1 = (n + 1) f_0{}^1$$

where $f_0{}^1$ is the fundamental frequency of the open pipe.
(c) Account for the fact that the note from an open pipe gives a richer note than that from a closed pipe.∎

Q 2.38 Self-assessment question
(a) Two organ pipes with closed ends are sounded together, and eight beats per second are heard. If the shorter pipe is 0.50 m long, what is the length of the other pipe?
(b) A loudspeaker is connected to a signal generator and placed over the open end of a vertical tube 0.40 m long which is open at the other end. At what frequencies will resonance occur, as the frequency of the note emitted is increased from 400 Hz to 1800 Hz?
(You may ignore any end-corrections. The speed of sound in air is 340 m s^{-1}.)∎

Resonance tube experiment
The resonance tube provides a convenient method for determining the speed of sound in an air column by an *indirect* method (i.e. from the product of frequency and wavelength).

Q 2.39 Self-assessment question
The results shown in table 2.2 were obtained using a resonance tube closed at one end. The driving force was a loudspeaker which was connected to a signal generator. f is the frequency of the signal generator and l is the length of the air column at which the first position of resonance occurred for that frequency. The temperature of the air was 290 K.

Table 2.2

f/Hz	500	550	600	650	700
l/mm	155	138	130	112	103

(a) Plot these results so as to obtain a straight line graph.
(b) Explain why the graph does not pass through the origin and estimate the radius of the tube.
(c) Calculate the speed of sound in air at a temperature of 273 K.∎

Wind instruments
To produce sound from a wind instrument, a driving vibration sets up resonant vibrations in the air column. The complex sound produced contains a whole series of harmonics though, as we have discovered, only the odd harmonics can be present in the sound from a closed pipe.

The driving vibration in an oboe is provided by making a double reed vibrate, a trumpeter uses his lips to produce this driving vibration and in organ pipes a sharp edge or metal reeds are used. The quality of the sound produced will depend on
1   the shape of the vibrating air column,
2   the material of the instrument and the thickness of the material,
3   the kind of driving vibration used,
4   the player, who controls the air pressure and the pressure on the vibrating reed.

How is the pitch varied? A bugler can produce only a few notes from his simple instrument. By the way he blows (increasing his lip pressure) he can make the air column produce not only the fundamental but higher and higher harmonics in the series f, $2f$, $3f$, etc., but he cannot produce a note of frequency $3f/2$. The complete range of notes can only be produced by using a trumpet, in which the length of the pipe can be varied by opening one or more of the three valves on the instrument. In other wind instruments the pitch of the fundamental frequency is controlled by opening and closing holes along the length of the air column though, even in this case, higher frequencies can be obtained by the way the player blows.

Questions on objectives

1 Explain what is meant by a stationary wave.

A stationary sinusoidal transverse wave is set up in a string so that there are nodes at the ends and mid-point only. The displacement of each point on the string is a maximum when $t = 0$. Draw, on the same diagram, the positions of the string at $t = 0$, $t = T/8$, $t = T/4$, $t = 3T/8$, $t = T/2$, where T is the period.

(objectives 1, 3 and 7)

2 The speed of sound in a gas is given by the equation $c = \sqrt{\gamma p/\rho}$, where p is the pressure, ρ the density and γ is a constant appropriate to the gas.
(a) Show, by the method of dimensional analysis, that this equation is dimensionally correct.
(b) Deduce the effect on the speed of sound in a gas of (i) a change in pressure and (ii) a change in temperature.
(c) If the speed of sound in air at 273 K is 330 m s^{-1}, find the speed of sound in air at 290 K.

(objectives 6 and 10)

3 Describe and explain, with the aid of a suitable diagram, the motion of the air in a tube open at both ends and vibrating in its fundamental mode.

(objective 8)

4 The speed of a transverse wave along a string is given by $c = \sqrt{T/\mu}$, where T is the tension and μ the mass per unit length.
(a) Explain how reflection may give rise to transverse stationary waves in a stretched string of length l.
(b) Use the above expression for the speed to derive the frequency f of the fundamental mode of vibration.

(objectives 4 and 7)

5 Explain why the fundamental frequency and quality of a note from an open pipe differ from those of the note produced under similar conditions from a closed pipe of the same length.

(objectives 1 and 8)

6 Compare the properties of a stationary wave pattern in air with those of a progressive sound wave in respect of (i) amplitude, (ii) pressure variation, (iii) phase.

(objective 5)

7 In a resonance tube experiment, a series of results for the minimum length l of the air column in a resonance tube closed at one end, resonating to a loudspeaker at various frequencies f, were obtained. A graph is plotted of l (y-axis) against $1/f$ (x-axis).
(a) Sketch the graph you would expect to obtain.
(b) How would you obtain a value for the speed of sound in an air column from the graph?
(c) What is the significance of the intercept on the l axis ($1/f = 0$)?

(objective 9)

8 A loudspeaker is connected to a signal generator and placed several metres from a smooth wall. The signal generator is switched on and the frequency is adjusted to 6.0×10^2 Hz.
(a) Assuming that the loudspeaker is positioned so that waves are incident normally on the wall, what happens to the sound waves at the wall?
(b) Assuming no energy loss at the wall, explain what happens to the air molecules in a region up to 1.5 m from the wall.

(objectives 3 and 4)

9 For an air column up to 2.00 m long, with a closed (but adjustable) end, find the lengths at which resonance with a 280 Hz tuning fork will occur. You may ignore end-corrections.
(Speed of sound in air = 340 m s^{-1}.)
(objective 10)

10 Two organ pipes X and Y produce first overtones of the same frequency at the same temperature. If X is an open pipe, calculate the ratios of (i) the length of X to that of Y, and (ii) the fundamental frequency of X to that of Y. You may ignore end-corrections.
(objective 10)

11 A steel wire of diameter 0.50 mm is clamped tightly between two supports 20 cm apart under a tension of 100 N. Find the frequency of the lowest note that the string emits when it is plucked.
(Density of steel = 7.9 × 10^3 kg m^{-3}.)
(objective 10)

12 EXTENSION
For a medium in which a sinusoidal progressive wave is being propagated, the displacement y at time t of a particle in the medium at a distance x from the origin is given by the formula

$$y = a \sin 2\pi f(t - x/c)$$

(a) Define the quantities represented by a, f and c.
(b) How do you interpret the following equation?

$$y = a \sin 2\pi f(t + x/c)$$

(c) When the two progressive waves represented by the equations in (a) and (b) are superimposed, the equation of the resultant displacement y is given by

$$y = a \cos 2\pi f(x/c) \sin 2\pi ft$$

Show that this represents a stationary wave system.
(objective 11)

Chapter

Aim

The aim of this chapter is to develop an understanding of the diffraction effects produced by light waves, and to discover how diffraction and interference phenomena provide a means of measuring microscopic lengths. To achieve these aims, you will observe diffraction effects at single and multiple apertures, develop hypotheses to explain these diffraction patterns, study and interpret evidence about the spectra of radiation from different light sources and study applications in which the wave properties of light provide us with very precise measuring instruments.

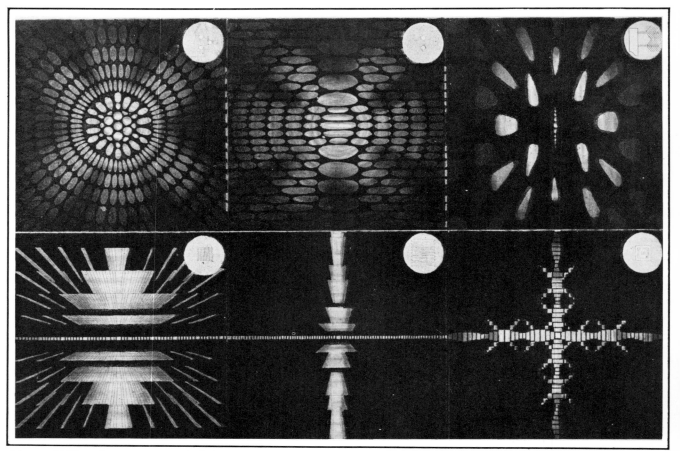

Above. Diffraction patterns of different shaped apertures observed and drawn from observations in the 19th C before the invention of photography.

Chapter

Objectives

When you have completed this chapter you should be able to:

1 Use the following scientific terms correctly: diffraction, diffraction pattern, zero order image, first order maximum, Rayleigh's criterion, transmission grating, spectrometer, pure spectrum, emission and absorption spectra, line spectrum, continuous spectrum, monochromatic source, thin film interference, contour fringes, optical path, optical wedge, Newton's rings.

2 Define resolving power and use it in discussing images formed by telescopes and the eye.

3 Describe briefly the diffraction patterns formed by a straight edge and a circular obstacle.

4 Describe and explain the diffraction pattern of a single slit and list the factors which influence the angular separation between central maximum and first minimum.

5 Describe and explain the main features of the pattern obtained when light passes through a diffraction grating.

6 Derive and use an equation relating the wavelength with the angular separation of the diffracted spectra and the coarseness of the grating.

7 Outline an experiment to determine the wavelength of light using a transmission grating.

8 Outline the requirements for producing a pure spectrum using (i) a prism, and (ii) a diffraction grating. Distinguish between the spectra produced in each case.

9 Describe a method for producing (i) an emission spectrum and (ii) an absorption spectrum, using a prism or a grating.

10 Describe and explain the formation of fringes in an optical wedge illuminated normally, and use the observations to measure thickness.

11 Give a simple account of the formation of colours in thin films.

Experiments in chapter 3

VW 11 Waves through holes
(1½ hours)
VW 12 Resolving power
(½ hour)
VW 13 Waves past obstacles
(1 hour)
VW 14 Observing diffraction patterns and measuring wavelength
(1½ hours)
VW 15 Observing spectra
(¾ hour)
VW 16 Lloyd's mirror interference
(¾ hour)

Study time: 2½ weeks

References

Bolton	Chapter 6
Duncan FWA	Chapter 8
Millar	Chapters 25, 26, 27
Nelkon	Chapter 28
Wenham	Chapter 23
Whelan	Chapters 14, 38, 39

3.1 Introduction

All measurement depends on having a suitable 'measuring stick' available. In the laboratory and workshop we use tape-measures, rulers and micrometers. In surveying, our measuring stick is the known distance between reference points (triangulation points). In astronomy, the diameter of the earth's orbit is a vital 'yardstick' for measuring small astronomical distances, though for very large astronomical distances we have to rely on the speed of distant nebulae, revealed by the Doppler shift, to estimate their distance away.

In your earlier study of interference of waves you have observed how minute changes (of less than a wavelength) in the path travelled by waves affects the kind of interference produced. These interference effects, which depend on the wavelength of the waves, enable us to use the precise and constant wavelengths of light emitted from glowing atomic vapours as the 'yardstick' for microscopic measurement. The standard unit of length—the metre—was once defined in terms of the length of a particular bar of a platinum-iridium alloy, but interference methods have been used to redefine the metre in terms of the wavelength in vacuum of the red-orange line in the spectrum of krypton-86.

In this chapter we discuss how light waves are used to measure the expansion of crystals, the flatness of optical surfaces, the surface structure of minerals, the thickness of very thin layers, and study the diffraction and interference effects which provide these methods of measuring.

3.2 Light through apertures

You are familiar with the idea that ripples on water spread out after passing through a small gap. *Diffraction* is the term used to describe this effect, and it is a property of all waves. We take for granted the diffraction of sound waves which spread around obstacles and round the corners of gaps, like doorways. Equally, we accept that we cannot *see* around corners. Sound and light behave differently, yet we have evidence that sound and light are both waves and share wave properties. When we compare their wavelengths, it is not really surprising that they behave very differently.

Q 3.1 Self-assessment question
Compare the wavelength of a sound wave of frequency 170 Hz with that of light of average wavelength 5×10^{-7} m (speed of sound = 340 m s^{-1}). ■

Things appear a different size to sound waves and to light. It is obvious that if we are to observe any bending of light round obstacles or through gaps, we will have to go out of our way by looking for diffraction effects using very tiny apertures and obstacles. If diffraction effects occur in light, it is obviously of some significance because everything we see of the world is due to light passing through a small hole, the pupil of our eye.

E Experiment VW 11
Waves through holes
In this experiment you will investigate the effects produced when light passes through small apertures.

Q 3.2 Self-assessment question
Figure 3.1 shows the diffraction effects produced when water waves of different wavelengths pass through different gaps. Figures 3.1 a, b and c illustrate the same wavelength. Comment on the important features of each pattern and suggest what factor makes them different. State any agreement you have found in your experiment between the behaviour of light waves and ripples. ■

AV VW 6 Film loop
Diffraction: single slit
Changes in the pattern can be observed using single slits of different widths and different wavelengths of light.

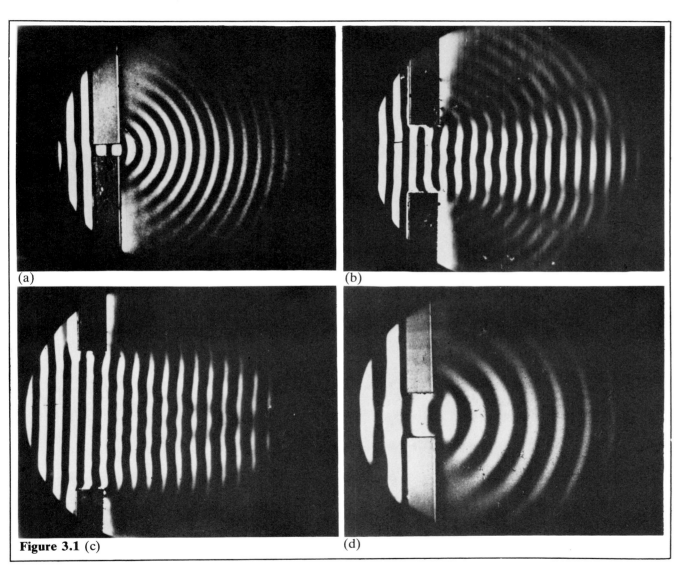

(a)

(b)

Figure 3.1 (c)

(d)

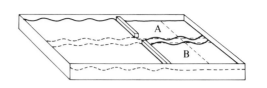

Figure 3.2 Imaginary water waves not diffracted at a gap

Q **3.3 Self-assessment question**
Figure 3.2 indicates how waves in a ripple tank would be expected to continue beyond a gap if *diffraction did not occur.*
(a)   Sketch the shape of the water surface between A and B according to figure 3.2. Explain in terms of the forces affecting the water surface why figure 3.2 describes an impossible situation.
(b)   How will the sideways spread be affected if the wave frequency is increased?■

Q **3.4 Self-assessment question**
If you wanted to carry out an experiment for observing the diffraction of sound waves at a slit, what kind of sound source would you use? How would you detect the sound diffracted, and what size of slit would you use?■

Defining diffraction

A series of single slit diffraction patterns are shown in figure 3.3. These were obtained by varying the width of the slit while keeping the wavelength of the light constant. Two obvious features of the single slit diffraction pattern are (i) the light waves extend into the region which would be in shadow if light travelled in straight lines, (ii) inside the shadow the light intensity varies, producing faint fringes.

You have already observed the interference fringes produced by superposition of waves from two coherent sources. The presence of bright and dark fringes in the single slit diffraction patterns (figure 3.3) suggests that perhaps even in this case we are observing an effect of superposition of wave energies. How can this be possible when we are only dealing with one wave from one aperture? It is true that there is only one aperture, but the wave energy reaching the screen is coming from different parts of the aperture and these separate energy sources combine to produce the observed diffraction effect.

Diffraction is defined as *the effect produced when waves from sources on the same wave front are superposed after the wavefront has been restricted by an obstacle or aperture.*

Q 3.5 Development question*

(a) What property of two waves should be added together when the waves are superposed?

(b) How can the resulting amplitude be found when two waves of the same frequency but different. phases are superposed?

(c) The intensity of light is defined as the rate at which light energy is radiated through unit area. What relationship relates intensity and amplitude for a light wave?∎

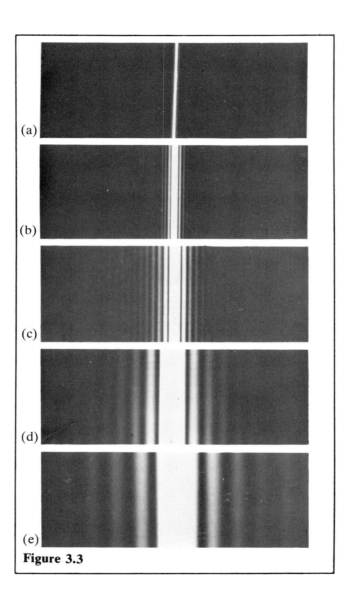

(a)

(b)

(c)

(d)

(e)

Figure 3.3

When light waves from different sources on the same wavefront are superposed, it is the wave *amplitudes* at particular points which must be added together (vectorially) but the results of this superposition are observed as a variation in light *intensity* which we call a diffraction pattern.

To predict the light intensity distribution produced by diffraction, Huygens' principle is applied. Before analysing diffraction at any slit, consider what happens at a very narrow slit.

Q 3.6 Self-assessment question

(a) Does any energy travel in the direction of the arrow (figure 3.4)? Justify your answer by sketching the wavefronts to the right of the slit and marking the directions in which energy is transmitted.

(b) What would happen if the barrier were removed? How does Huygens' principle support your answer?∎

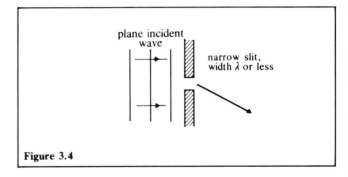

Figure 3.4

When a plane wave is diffracted at a very narrow slit (with a width of the order of a wavelength) we observe that a cylindrical diffracted wave spreads the energy out over a very large angle. To find out what happens at wider slits we can divide a wide slit into a number of narrow equal-width strips. Each strip can be considered as a very narrow slit radiating a cylindrical wave. The diffraction effect due to a wider slit can then be predicted by superimposing all these waves.

AV VW 7 Large transparencies
Diffraction at a single slit

Observe how the wave pattern changes as we superimpose waves from the centre and extreme edges of the slit. Locate the directions in which the separate wavelets are in phase and add up to produce a new straight wavefront. The tangent to these separate wavelets will indicate the new strong wavefronts. What kind of diffraction pattern is predicted by this construction?

Q 3.7 Development question*

In this question we consider the wave energy diffracted *in a particular direction* making angle θ with the straight-through direction when a *plane wave* is incident at a slit. You will find the value of θ at which minimum brightness occurs.

(a) The plane wavefront reaching the aperture (figure 3.5) is divided into many pairs of equal width strips each radiating waves: k and p are such a pair. Strip k is at one edge of the slit and strip p is just below the mid-point. What is the distance between k and p, l and q, and m and r?

(b) If energy travels from the slit at an angle θ_1 to the original direction, express the path difference in terms of a and θ_1 for waves from k and p travelling in directions kK and pP.

(c) For this particular angle θ_1 the path difference for waves from k and p is $\lambda/2$. What will be the effect on a distant screen where waves from k and p combine after travelling at angle θ_1 with the original wave direction?

(d) What will be the effect on the screen for waves from l and q travelling in the same direction?

(e) The effect of light from the whole slit can be found by adding up the effects due to all the pairs of narrow strips, each $a/2$ apart. What will be the resulting effect on the screen produced by a wave diffracted in this direction?

(f) We have considered one particular value of diffracting angle θ_1 which produces zero light on the screen. Write down an expression linking λ, a, and θ_1.

(g) Give reasons for thinking that at all angles less than θ_1 there will be some light reaching the screen beyond the slit.

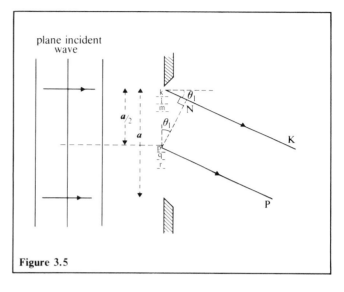

Figure 3.5

(h) Suppose light travelling from pairs of strips $a/4$ apart has a path difference $\lambda/2$ at an angle θ_2. Predict the effect produced by waves diffracted through θ_2, and give a relationship between θ_2, a and λ.

(i) Write down an equation predicting another direction θ_3 of the diffracted waves which produces a minimum.■

We can summarise our argument by stating that the angle between the centre of the pattern and the position of the first *minimum* is given by $\sin \theta_1 = \lambda/a$. This angle is important because it tells us the angular spread ($2\theta_1$) which contains most of the energy of the wave.

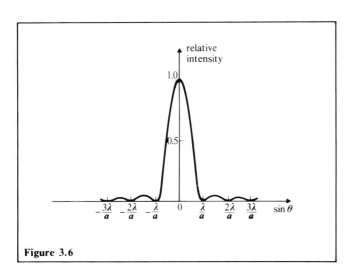

Figure 3.6

Figure 3.6 shows how the light intensity varies in different directions and emphasises that most of the energy in the diffraction pattern from a single slit is contained within the region of the central maximum. Note that the horizontal axis shows $\sin \theta$, but since the angles are very small this is almost identical to θ (in radians).

Q 3.8 Self-assessment question
If the width of the slit is large compared with the wavelength, what can you say about the angular spread of the central maximum? In which direction does the light travel after passing through the slit?■

Q 3.9 Self-assessment question
If the slit width is equal to (i) 3λ, and (ii) λ, what is the angular spread of the central maximum in each case?■

Q 3.10 Self-assessment question
Sketch a possible shape for the graph of light intensity against $\sin \theta$ for a slit of width λ.■

Q 3.11 Self-assessment question
Figure 3.3 shows how the diffraction pattern changes as the width of the slit changes.
(a) Which pattern is produced by the narrowest slit?
(b) What sort of slit, if any, is used in figure 3.3a?
(c) If figure 3.3c is obtained using a slit of width 4λ, estimate the width of the slit in figure 3.3d.
(d) Do the relative widths of the central and other fringes in figure 3.3 agree with the graph in figure 3.6?■

It is useful to divide diffraction effects into two groups (i) Fraunhöfer and (ii) Fresnel (see figure 3.7).

Fraunhöfer diffraction patterns are produced by the diffraction of plane waves. In question 3.7 we analysed a Fraunhöfer single slit diffraction pattern since we assumed that plane waves were incident at the slit and we considered the resulting diffraction effect in a particular direction. Fraunhöfer diffraction is obtained when source and screen are a long way from the aperture or lenses are used.

Fresnel diffraction patterns are produced when source and observer are finite distances from the obstacle or aperture. The analysis of these effects is very complex and will not be considered in this course.

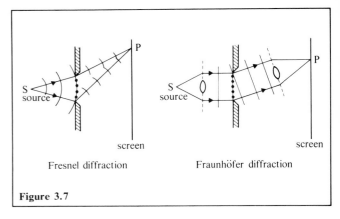

Fresnel diffraction   Fraunhöfer diffraction

Figure 3.7

Young's fringes
In Young's double slit experiment, light is diffracted through two narrow slits and a double slit interference pattern will be observed if the central maximum of each diffracted wave overlaps.

In chapter 3 of the Unit *Wave properties* we assumed the slits had negligible width and deduced that the variation in intensity in a double slit interference pattern would be as shown in figure 3.8a. In fact, because of the finite width a of the slits, the waves diffracted through the slits have an amplitude which varies with the angle of diffraction and the intensity curve for Young's slits is as shown in figure 3.8b. The separation of the interference fringes depends on the slit separation d while the width of the diffraction pattern depends on the width of the slits.

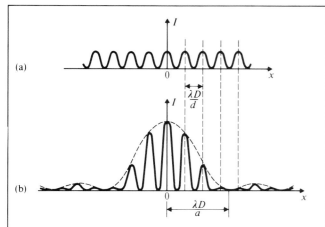

Figure 3.8 Intensity of Young's fringes across a screen, slit width a, slit separation d, distance from slit to screen D

Q **3.12 Self-assessment question**
A student rules a double slit on a painted glass slide but fails to observe Young's interference fringes. What advice would you give him for making double slits which would give a pattern bright enough to observe? Would you advise him to
(a) make the slits wider,
(b) make the slits narrow,
(c) rule the slits closer together?
Give reasons for the advice you give.∎

C **Computer Program**
INTERP
The program calculates intensity distribution curves due to superposition of waves (a) from two coherent point sources and (b) from two slits of finite width. The various factors which determine the intensity distribution are discussed.

3.3 Resolving power

Light through a hole, like our eye or a telescope, doesn't usually come from just one place. We observe patterns of stars, or the fine print in a book, and we want to see as much detail as possible. What effect has diffraction on the ability to see detail—to distinguish light from different places? This section will provide an answer to this question.

E **Experiment VW 12**
Resolving power
This experiment shows that what we see depends on the colour of the light used and the size of the hole we look through.

When you look at a row of bright filaments through a slit it is not always possible to see a row of separate sources. You are actually observing not a series of filaments but a series of diffraction patterns which may overlap so much that you cannot separate them. In this case we say the images are not *resolved*.

A point source viewed through a small circular aperture gives a circular diffraction pattern. The size of the pattern depends on the ratio λ/D (D = diameter of aperture). Figure 3.9 shows a point source and three pairs of point sources viewed through three different circular apertures. In (a) the opening is such that all three pairs of points are clearly resolved. Decreasing the size of the aperture increases the size of the diffraction pattern. In (b) the two upper pairs of points are clearly resolved whereas the lowest pair is near the limit of resolution. In (c) the lowest pair are not resolved, the middle pair are near the limit of resolution and the upper pair are still clearly resolved.

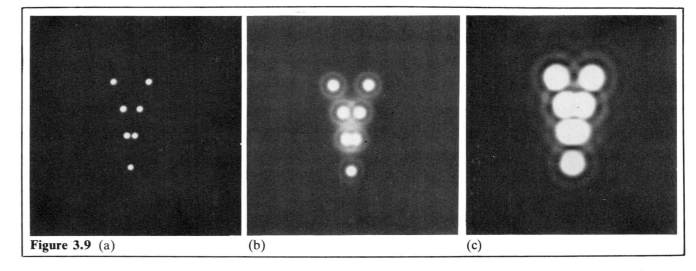

Figure 3.9 (a)   (b)   (c)

This means that optical instruments like microscopes, telescopes and eyes cannot produce a point image of a point object but only a diffraction pattern. The angular spread θ from the centre of this pattern to the first dark ring is given by the equation

$$\sin \theta = \frac{1.22\lambda}{D}$$

where λ is the wavelength of light and D is the diameter of the circular aperture.

For all the apertures we shall consider D is much bigger than λ and so $\sin \theta$ is very small and can be approximated to θ. In calculations on optical instruments you can simplify the expression further and use

$$\theta \approx \frac{\text{wavelength}}{\text{diameter}}$$

where θ is the angular separation between the centre and the first dark fringe. You should memorise this expression—you will need it in the questions which follow.

Q 3.13 Study question
Explain what is meant by Rayleigh's criterion for resolution illustrating your answer by appropriate light intensity graphs. Show how this leads to a way of assessing the resolving power of a telescope. ∎

Q 3.14 Self-assessment question
What quantity do you use for assessing resolving power? What happens to the resolving power of telescopes as the diameter of the objective lens is increased? ∎

Q 3.15 Self-assessment question
Why do you think astronomers photograph stars through a blue filter? ∎

Q 3.16 Self-assessment question
If a TV lens of diameter 7.5 cm is mounted on a satellite 300 km high to photograph the earth and the system uses light of wavelength 5.5×10^{-7} m, what is the smallest resolvable distance on the earth? ∎

Resolving power of the eye

What factors limit our ability to see things in fine detail? One factor is the diffraction effect at the pupil of our eye. The smallest angular separation θ between two 'just resolved' objects is approximately

$$\frac{(\text{wavelength of light})}{(\text{pupil diameter})} \text{ radian}$$

There is another factor which limits our ability to see fine detail. The brain builds up pictures from a multitude of signals from retinal nerve cells (rods and cones) just as a newspaper picture is built up of a host of black dots. The fine detail we see must be limited by the closeness of these retinal receptors.

These factors change with the light conditions. The pupil diameter varies. In normal lighting, the eye observes detail by focusing the image on the centre of the retina where receptors are closely packed. In dim light the other parts of the retina are used where receptors are more sensitive but more widely spaced.

Q 3.17 Development question*
(a) Taking 2 mm for the diameter of the eye pupil and 5×10^{-7} m for the wavelength of light, estimate the limit of resolution of the eye due to diffraction (i.e. the smallest distinguishable angular separation).
(b) If two objects subtend an angle of 4×10^{-4} radian at the eye and the distance from eye lens to retina is 20 mm, how far apart are the two images formed on the retina?
(c) In the central area of the retina the light receptors are 2×10^{-6} m apart. Is this spacing adequate to enable the eye to resolve two objects separated by the angle which you calculated in (a)?
(d) What other factors do you think may limit the ability of the eye to see fine details? ∎

It is probably true to say that for a normal eye all these limiting factors are well matched and an improvement in one limit would be worthless without changes in other factors.

Q 3.18 Self-assessment question
Give a reason why it may be easier to see fine detail on an object in moderately bright light than in very bright light. Suggest why resolution is poor in very dim light. ∎

Q 3.19 Development question*
A magnifying instrument like a telescope is designed to produce an image subtending an angle β at the eye which is greater than the angle α subtended at the eye by the original object.
Angular magnification or magnifying power $= \beta/\alpha$.
If α is the angular separation of two stars, β will be the angular separation of their images seen in the telescope.

(a) If a telescope objective has a diameter of 3.0 m, calculate the angular separation between two stars which can just be resolved taking the average value for the wavelength of light as 6×10^{-7} m.

(b) If the telescope produces an angular magnification of 500, what will the angle be at the eye between the two star images which are just resolved by the telescope?

(c) If the resolving power of the eye is 3×10^{-4} rad, will the two stars be seen as resolved objects by the eye?

(d) What magnifying power will produce rays subtended at the eye which enable the two stars to be just resolved?■

The telescope must be designed to provide a magnifying power which is appropriate for the diameter of its objective. If the magnifying power is less than the appropriate value the resolving power will be limited by the resolving power of the eye. Increasing the magnifying power above the appropriate value will not produce more detail. The observer will see a more magnified diffraction pattern but no greater detail. The only way to see greater detail in the picture will be to increase the size of the telescope objective.

According to a recent investigation by Cambridge University Physiology Department, television viewers can achieve an apparent improvement in picture quality by viewing the screen through a small hole (about 1 mm diameter)! This removes the visual 'noise' component from the picture. This noise component consists of very tiny dots which move at random in contrast with the useful picture information which is made up of larger components which move together. Because of diffraction at the pinhole, the tiny dots of the 'noise' will be seen as very diffuse diffraction patterns. Thus, the fine detail of the unwanted noise will not be resolved and the picture quality will be improved. Try it!

Q **3.20 Self-assessment question**
(a) Explain what would happen to the brightness of a television picture if the screen is viewed through a 1 mm diameter pinhole instead of directly.

(b) Suggest how the quality of the picture might change if a 0.5 mm diameter viewing hole was used instead of a 1 mm hole. What determines the optimum size of viewing hole?■

E **Experiment VW 13**
Waves past obstacles
The diffraction of ripples and light waves due to obstacles is observed.

In this experiment you have observed diffraction patterns at finite viewing distances. These are called *Fresnel* patterns and figure 3.10 shows the Fresnel diffraction pattern of a small circular obstacle. In this case, there is a bright spot at the centre of the shadow. You have found that the kind of pattern produced depends on the viewing position, and it can be shown that the pattern produced also depends on the nearness of the source to the aperture or obstacle. This is characteristic of Fresnel diffraction.

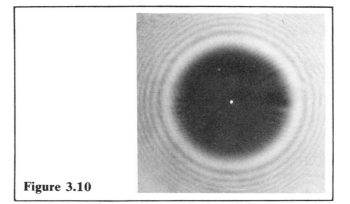

Figure 3.10

Q **3.21 Self-assessment question**
If you live some distance from a building housing a disco, you will almost certainly hear the music even though there are houses between you and the disco! Why is this possible? The low bass notes will be much more audible than other sounds. Suggest a possible explanation of this effect.■

3.4 Waves through many slits

In the last section you observed the diffraction pattern produced by a single slit, whilst in the Unit *Wave properties* you observed the interference pattern produced when light passed through two slits. What is the difference between an interference pattern and a diffraction pattern? None really! For historical reasons, the pattern produced by superposing waves from two or more separate coherent sources is usually called an *interference* pattern. The variation of intensity produced by superposing light from different parts of a continuous wave which has been obstructed is called *diffraction*. So we speak of the *interference* pattern produced by two vibrating dippers in a ripple tank, and the *diffraction* pattern from a single slit.

Q **3.22 Study question**
Figure 3.8b shows the intensity graph produced when a plane wave is diffracted by two slits. Now study intensity graphs or photographs in your reference texts of diffraction patterns for three or more equidistant slits. Comment briefly on how an increase in the number of slits affects
(a) the spacing of the maxima,
(b) the sharpness of the maxima.■

Diffraction of a plane wave incident at a narrow slit produces cylindrical waves which we could draw as circles. A whole series of narrow slits would produce a set of overlapping cylindrical waves. Figure 3.11 shows the interfering waves from a series of point sources (or narrow slits).

Look obliquely along the diagram (figure 3.11) from the bottom edge. Can you see some strong wavefronts travelling across the page parallel to the line of slits (figure 3.12a)? This suggests that diffraction will produce some strong undeviated waves which we will call *zero order* waves.

Turn the diagram round a little and observe a series of strong wavefronts travelling slightly oblique to AB (figure 3.12b). We can call this set a *first order* set.

Turn the book further and other more oblique strong wavefronts can be observed diffracted on both sides of the central zero order waves.

A transmission diffraction grating allows light waves to pass through a series of equidistant fine slits and produces a series of diffracted maxima (figure 3.13).

Q **3.23 Study question**
(a) Using figure 3.14, and considering the superposition of waves from adjacent slits, deduce a relationship between the slit separation s in a grating, the wavelength λ of the light and the angle θ_1 through which the intense first order waves are diffracted.
(b) What equation will link θ_2, λ and s for the second order maxima?
(c) Write down a general equation for the mth order maxima. ∎

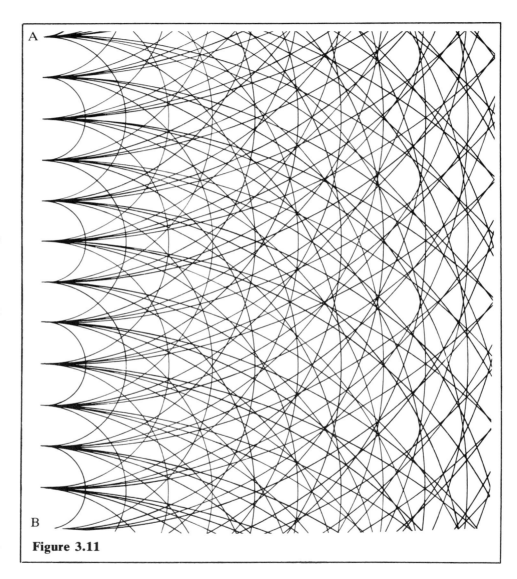

Figure 3.11

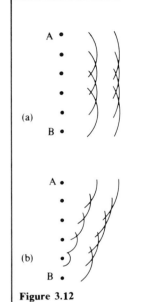

Figure 3.12

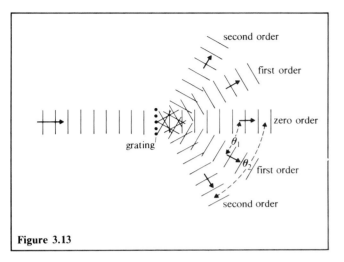

Figure 3.13

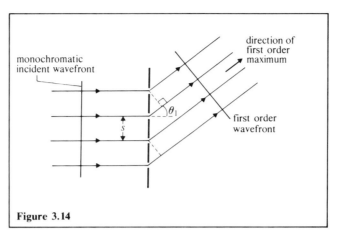

Figure 3.14

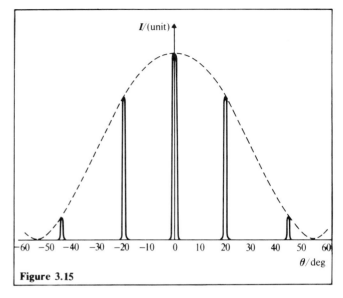

Figure 3.15

Q 3.24 Self-assessment question

Measure angles θ_1 and θ_2, s and λ for the circular waves in figure 3.11 and check whether the equations you have deduced agree with your observations of this diagram. ■

E Experiment VW 14
Observing diffraction patterns and measuring wavelength

In this experiment you will observe the patterns produced by fine and coarse gratings and use a fine grating to measure the wavelength of light.

Q 3.25 Self-assessment question

Figure 3.15 shows the intensity graph for a diffraction grating illuminated normally by monochromatic light. The sharp peaks of the pattern of superposition are enclosed within the diffraction envelope produced by each slit.

(a) If the grating has 6000 lines per cm, calculate the wavelength of the light.

(b) Will third order maxima be visible? Explain.

(c) Estimate from the graph the width of each slit in the grating. ■

Q 3.26 Self-assessment question

A gramophone record will act as a reflection grating. To observe the effect, the reflection of a distant fluorescent tube lamp must be viewed very obliquely in the record. Why do you think the pattern is only seen when viewed obliquely? Which direction must the fluorescent tube point in for the best results? Draw a sketch and try the experiment if you can find time. ■

Q 3.27 Self-assessment question

A distant sodium street lamp is viewed through a piece of muslin and two sets of five equally spaced lamps are seen in rows, each row at right angles to one set of the threads of the material. The outermost lamps appear to be separated by an angle of 0.01 radian. Estimate the number of threads in a metre of the material, assuming the wavelength of light is 6×10^{-7} m. ■

AV VW 8 Slideset
Diffraction patterns

View more diffraction patterns to supplement your direct observations in experiments.

Comprehension exercise

Diffraction rules the waves

Most ideas for the generation of power from waves have centred around various oscillating mechanisms which tap the energy from the waveform itself and involve still developing technology which could prove too costly or complicated. An approach which is both simple and uses proven technology has, however, been suggested by the Central Institute for Industrial Research in Oslo. The researchers have proposed that a series of blocks could be moored offshore, in such a position that waves are diffracted to concentrate most of their energy onto a stretch of coastline approximately 400 metres long. The waves, now 15–30 metres high, would be funnelled into a channel leading to a reservoir which could be as much as 100 metres above sea level. Generation of electricity would follow by a conventional hydroelectric power station. The Norwegians estimate that such a power station, utilising approximately 10 kilometres of the Norwegian coastline for wave gathering, could have an annual output of 800-2000 gigawatt hours. (By comparison, Oslo, with a population of 472,000, uses 2900 GW h per year.)

The Institute is recommending that an experimental wave power station should be constructed in one of the bays of the Oslo Fjord. If this is successful a prototype power station could be in use by 1985.

(*New Scientist,* 9th February 1978)

Questions*
1 What important quantities must be known before it is possible to design a grating?

2 Assuming all the energy of the waves along a 10 km stretch of coastline is used to produce waves 20 m high (amplitude 10 m) concentrated along a 400 m length of beach, estimate what value this implies as typical for the amplitude of a sea wave off Norway. Is this value realistic?

3 If a diffraction maximum is to be produced at F (figure 3.16b) by constructive superposition, suggest values for the lengths AF, BF, CF, etc. Will the grating have equally-spaced slits? Explain.

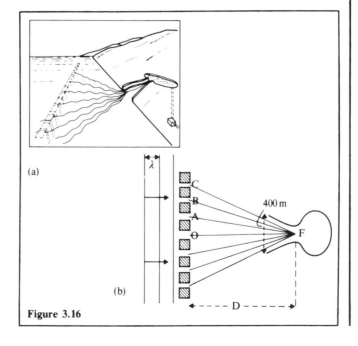

(a)

(b)

Figure 3.16

3.5 Spectra

How is it possible to find out what kind of light is being emitted by a source? Our eye responds to a range of waves whose wavelengths in air vary between about 4×10^{-7} m and 7×10^{-7} m. Through our eyes we receive the total message—the summed up effect of all the different component wavelengths in the light which gives the source its particular colour and brightness. But if we want to identify the different components present in the light we need to be able to separate the components. The diffraction grating provides us with a very convenient 'separator'.

You have looked at a light source through a diffraction grating and will have observed that (except for the zero order beam) the angle at which the light is diffracted strongly depends on its wavelength. A source emitting several wavelengths produces diffracted beams which are separated into component wavelengths. This separation of light into component colours is an example of *dispersion.*

A rainbow is formed by dispersion when light from the sun is refracted and reflected internally by raindrops. Isaac Newton studied the dispersion of light by a prism and later Joseph Fraunhöfer began to develop simple gratings in order to observe dispersion effects. The band of colour produced by dispersion is an example of a *spectrum.* It is really a series of different coloured images of the source.

**E Experiment VW 15
Observing spectra**
You will compare the spectra of different light sources and note the differences between spectra produced by grating and prism.

Obtaining a good spectrum

To analyse light effectively, we need to produce a pure spectrum, and also obtain a lot of dispersion so that very close wavelengths can be separated or resolved. A *pure spectrum* is produced when there is no overlapping of colours because every component wavelength produces a separate non-overlapping image of the slit. A spectrometer is an instrument for producing and measuring pure spectra.

Q **3.28 Study question***
Think what components you would need to obtain a good spectrum—as close as possible to 'pure'. Study your books to find how a pure spectrum is produced.
(a) List the apparatus needed to produce a pure spectrum.
(b) State the function of each component.
(c) Show by a diagram how they should be arranged. (Check your list with the answer provided.)■

Q **3.29 Study question**
Why are special achromatic lenses used in a spectrometer?■

Q **3.30 Self-assessment question**
Why do you get a reasonable spectrum in experiment VW 15 without using a lens? Why do you use a distant source?■

Q **3.31 Self-assessment question**
Can you suggest any reasons why a grating is often preferred to a prism in modern spectrometers?■

Q **3.32 Self-assessment question**
(a) What angle of dispersion is there between red ($\lambda = 7.0 \times 10^{-7}$ m) and blue light ($\lambda = 4.0 \times 10^{-7}$ m) in the first order spectrum produced by a diffraction grating with 6000 lines per cm?
(b) At what angle does the second order red image appear?
(c) Is there any overlap between the second and third order spectra?■

Q **3.33 Study question**
Describe a method for measuring the wavelength of light from a sodium lamp using a diffraction grating and a spectrometer. Outline the adjustment of the spectrometer and state what readings are taken in measuring the results.■

Types of spectra

How can we classify spectra? The light from a glowing substance produces an *emission spectrum*. When white light passes through an absorbing medium like a coloured filter an *absorption spectrum* of the material is produced. This absorption can also occur in liquids and gases and can occur even when the gas is glowing.

A study of how spectra are produced leads to important theories about atomic structure which are discussed in the Unit *Electrons and the nucleus*.

AV **VW 9 Slide set**
Types of spectra
The colour slides show examples of the different types of optical spectra and after you have viewed them and read the accompanying notes, you should answer the following study question.

Q **3.34 Study question**
Make notes on how spectra are classified into line, band and continuous spectra, indicating why the different names are appropriate and stating what kinds of sources produce each type.■

Q **3.35 Self-assessment question**
If light from a white hot filament is focused on a sodium flame and then enters a spectrometer, an unexpected spectrum is produced. Instead of seeing all the colours in white light with extra bright yellow lines from the glowing sodium, the spectrum has two close *dark* lines in the yellow region. Suggest an explanation of this effect.■

If a spectrometer is available, examine the spectrum for yourself by setting up the apparatus as shown in figure 3.17.

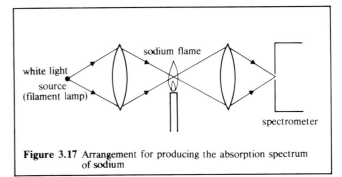

Figure 3.17 Arrangement for producing the absorption spectrum of sodium

Q 3.36 Study question*

(a) What kind of spectrum is the sun's spectrum?
(b) What are Fraunhöfer lines and what causes them?
(c) Suggest a reason why the darkness of some of the lines varies at different times.
(d) How can the spectrum emitted by the sun be reconciled with the idea that the sun is so hot that it must be gaseous?■

We know from the type of emission or absorption spectrum produced whether the light has been emitted or absorbed by atomic vapours, molecular vapours, liquids or solids. Much more significantly, the uniqueness of each line or band spectrum indicates that the light has been emitted or absorbed by a particular element or compound. This study of spectra provides a versatile technique for analysing substances. By using photographic or photocell detectors, which are extremely sensitive, the method can detect and measure the proportion of an element present in a mixture to one part in a million. The spectrum of the incandescent vapour of the substance being analysed can be obtained using a metal or carbon arc lamp or a discharge tube. Substances may also be analysed from their absorption spectra and this method is particularly important for biological material or foodstuffs. Many of the important characteristic lines are in the ultra-violet region, whilst infrared spectra are important in learning about the bonding and structure of complex molecules. Further applications will be discussed in chapter 4 and in the Unit *Electrons and the nucleus*.

3.6 Measurement by interference of light waves

Glowing atomic gases produce line spectra. Each line represents an energy emission whose frequency is constant and absolutely unique to that particular gas; so unique and constant that we can use such a frequency to standardise and measure time. 1 second is the time for 9 192 631 770 vibrations of a particular energy radiation of the caesium-133 atom!

Q 3.37 Self-assessment question

Why is the wavelength of radiation not constant, as is the frequency?■

The wavelengths (in vacuum) of light from glowing gases also provide us with standard lengths which can be accurately compared with the standard metre which is now defined as 1 650 763.73 wavelengths in vacuum of the red-orange line in the spectrum of krypton-86 vapour.

But how can we measure something as small as the wavelength of light? With the help of the principle of superposition this is possible. You have already seen how changing the path difference between two waves by as small a distance as half a wavelength (3×10^{-7} m) can change brightness into darkness. This means that interference effects can provide us with an extremely finely graduated measuring scale.

Changing the optical path

If two coherent light sources emit waves, the interference effect will depend on the effective path difference. This is because difference in path length introduces a difference in travelling time for the two waves and this determines the phase relationship between the waves arriving together and being superposed.

The next two questions explain the term *optical path* and show how it is different from the *geometrical path*.

Q 3.38 Development question*

S_1 and S_2 (figure 3.18) are two coherent sources producing an interference pattern on the screen. Consider the change in the interference effect at P when a slab of optically dense material (refractive index n) is introduced into the path $S_1 P$.
(a) What will happen to the time taken for the wave to travel from S_1 to P when the slab is introduced? Give a reason.

(b) Show that $\dfrac{\lambda_{air}}{\lambda_{slab}} = n$

The actual distance travelled by the wave is unchanged but the time taken has increased. The time interval for transit through the slab is greater than the time interval for transit through the same thickness of air. The reduced wave speed in the slab produces a decrease in wavelength and the effective path—the optical path —has been increased.
(c) What length of air has the same optical path as a thickness t of the medium?
(d) What change in optical path occurs as a result of replacing a length t of air with a length t of material of refractive index n?
(e) Before the slab was introduced the path lengths were equal for a point O and there was a bright fringe at O. Suppose point P was previously the position of the thirtieth fringe from O. What was the path difference ($S_2P - S_1P$) before the slab was introduced?

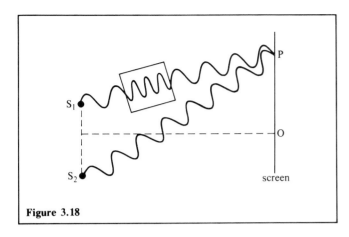

Figure 3.18

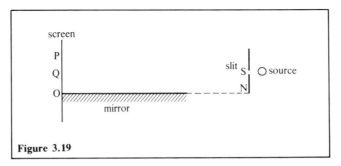

Figure 3.19

(f) When the slab was introduced, the fringe which was at O moved to P. What change in optical path difference occurred when the slab was introduced?

(g) If $n = 1.5$ for the slab and the wavelength of the source is 6×10^{-7} m, what value does this give for the thickness of the slab?

Note: To make quantitative observations of this effect, a white light source is used because with this source the displaced zero order fringe can be easily identified. ■

Phase change on reflection

One other factor makes the optical path different from the geometrical path—*phase change due to reflection.* The arrangement shown in figure 3.19, called Lloyd's mirror, provides evidence of this. A pattern of fringes can be produced using a single slit S and a reflector. Waves from the slit arriving at the screen after being reflected from the mirror are superposed with waves travelling directly to the screen.

$\mathbf{Q}$ **3.39 Development question***
(a) Slit S in figure 3.19 acts as one of the coherent sources. Where is the other coherent source located?
(b) Where is the geometrical path difference greater, at P or at Q?
(c) What is the geometrical path difference at O?
(d) What kind of interference fringe do you predict will be at O, bright or dark?

Experiment shows that there is a dark zero order fringe at O. This is evidence that the reflected wave has undergone a phase change of π rad on reflection, producing the same effect as a change in optical path length of $\lambda/2$. Once again, the optical path is not the same as the geometrical path.

(e) How could you arrange to move the zero order dark fringe from O to some point P on the screen?
(f) Using monochromatic light it is not really possible to pick out the central zero dark fringe—to do this you need to use a white light source. Explain this statement and describe briefly what this fringe pattern will look like if a white light source is used.
(g) If the distance from slit S to N is 0.5 mm, OP is 2.5 mm, the distance from the slit to the screen is 1 m and the wavelength of the light used is 5×10^{-7} m. What will an observer see at P? ■

When a wave pulse reaches a boundary between a light and heavy spring, the pulse is reflected with a phase change of π rad if it is travelling from the light to the heavy spring but there is no phase change at a heavy-to-light spring boundary (see Unit *Wave properties*, figure 1.8). This is a perfect analogy of the behaviour of light waves. Light reflected in a rare medium at a boundary with a denser medium is reflected with a phase change of π rad but there is no phase change on reflection when the light is travelling from a dense to an optically rarer medium.

$\mathbf{E}$ **Experiment VW 16**
Lloyd's mirror interference

An interference pattern is produced by superposition of two light waves from the same small source, one wave being reflected at a shallow angle from a plane surface and the other wave travelling directly from source to observer.

Interference in an air wedge

The interference patterns of light waves discussed so far have been produced by division of a primary wavefront to produce two coherent sources (e.g. parts of the wave were transmitted through two slits). The waves from the two sources took separate paths before being superposed. This kind of interference is often called *interference by division of the wavefront*. Interference effects are also produced when a wave divides into two less intense waves at a boundary and these waves travel by different paths before recombining. This is *interference by division of amplitude* and can occur when the light comes from a large (extended) source.

Q 3.40 Development question*

Figure 3.20a shows the paths of two reflected waves. Part of the incident wave is reflected at the top of the air wedge (wave 1) and another part travels through the air film and is reflected at the bottom of the air film (wave 2). The two reflected waves will recombine in the observer's eye if he looks at the film directly or through a microscope.

(a) At point A the thickness of the film is $\lambda/4$. What is the geometrical path difference for waves 1 and 2? (We can assume normal reflection—at right angles to the boundary.)

(b) Is there a phase change on reflection for both waves 1 and 2?

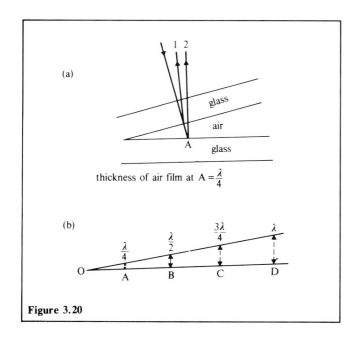

Figure 3.20

(c) The film appears bright at A when viewed from above. Explain.

(d) A, B, C, D are points in the film where the thickness is as shown in figure 3.20b. What kind of interference is produced at B, C, D and O?

(e) If the distance between adjacent bright fringes is x, show that $\tan \theta = \lambda/2x$. Hence show that the fringes are equidistant. ∎

Each fringe in the air wedge passes through points of equal thickness and so the fringes are called *fringes of equal thickness* or *contour fringes*.

Q 3.41 Self-assessment question

The fringes in an air wedge are 0.4 mm apart. If water of refractive index $n = 4/3$ is introduced between the slides, what will be the fringe separation? ∎

Q 3.42 Self-assessment question

Two glass slides in contact along one edge are separated by a piece of metal foil 12.5 cm from the edge. Interference fringes parallel to the line of contact are observed in reflected light of wavelength 5.46×10^{-7} m and are found to be 1.50 mm apart. Find the thickness of the foil. ∎

The most famous fringes of equal thickness are those first observed by Newton and known as *Newton's rings*. They are formed by interference in a film between a plane glass surface and the surface of a weak converging lens.

Q 3.43 Study question

Sketch the experimental arrangement for observing Newton's rings. Show how the light travels between source and microscope. Say which point the microscope is focused on and what an observer would see on looking at the centre of the pattern. ∎

Q 3.44 Self-assessment question

What will happen to the pattern if a few drops of liquid are placed between the lens and the glass plate in Newton's rings apparatus? Does this provide a good method for measuring refractive index? Mention one advantage of this method. ∎

The optical wedge provides a very convenient method of measuring the thickness of a thin material used to separate two glass slides forming an air wedge.

Q 3.45 Self-assessment question

A crystal can change in thickness when heated or when a strong electric field is applied across it. Suggest how an interference method can be used to measure this small change in thickness. ∎

Figure 3.21 shows two exciting applications of thin film interference. Figure 3.21a shows the smooth curvature of a piece of moon dust and figure 3.21b shows the contour fringes formed between an optical flat and a diamond surface. Notice how the fringes indicate the ridges in the surface.

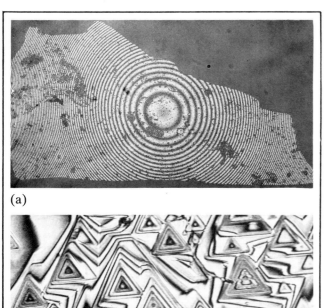

(a)

(b)

Figure 3.21

Comprehension Exercise
(London A level paper III June 1977)

An experiment was carried out to determine the radius of curvature, R, of a spherical lens surface. The surface was placed on a plane piece of glass, it was illuminated normally with light of wavelength λ, and the resulting interference fringes (Newton's rings) were observed. The fringes were concentric circles.

The observer chose a particular bright fringe a little way out from the centre of the fringes and measured its diameter. He called this fringe number 0. Working away from the centre he measured the diameters of every tenth fringe, i.e. he measured the diameters of fringes numbered 10, 20, 30, 40 and 50. He obtained the following results:

Fringe number, p	Fringe diameter/mm
0	5·94
10	8·29
20	10·11
30	11·61
40	12·99
50	14·20

It may be shown that if n is the number of a fringe *counting from the centre of the fringes* its diameter, d, is given by

$$d^2 = 4n\lambda R - 2\lambda R \qquad (1)$$

It was not easy to determine n, and this is why the observer started counting fringes a little way out from the centre where they were sharper and easier to measure.

We may write

$$n = p + n_0$$

where n_0 is the (unknown) number of the first fringe measured by the observer, counting from the centre.

We then have

$$d^2 = 4\lambda R(p + n_0) - 2\lambda R \qquad (2)$$

If d is plotted against p, the slope S of the resulting curve is given by

$$S = 2\lambda R/d \qquad (3)$$

The wavelength of light used was $5\cdot893 \times 10^{-4}$ mm.

Questions

1 Plot a graph of d as ordinate against the corresponding value of p as abscissa and determine the value of its slope S at a suitable point. Record the value of d at this point.

2 From equation (3) and the given value of λ calculate a value for R.

3 Draw up a table of d^2 and the corresponding values of p. Plot a graph of d^2 against p. From this graph obtain a further value for the radius R, and also determine the value of n_0.

4 You have now calculated two values of R. Which value do you consider to be the more reliable, that obtained in question 2 or that obtained in question 3? Give your reasons.

Colours in thin films

The colours of oil films on water, soap bubbles and insects' wings are all the result of interference effects.

If white light is reflected at the two sides of a film, certain colours will be reflected strongly at different directions if the path difference between the two reflected waves produces constructive superposition. The path difference depends on the thickness and viewing position (see figure 3.22); the colours will change with both these factors. You can test this statement for yourself by direct observation of (i) a drop of oil spreading over warm water, or (ii) a film of detergent solution formed on a wire frame which is held vertically until the film breaks.

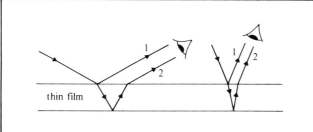

Figure 3.22 Change of path difference with viewing angle

Q 3.46 Self-assessment question

Figure 3.23 shows the interference effects produced in a vertical soap film illuminated with monochromatic light.
(a) Why are the bands of brightness horizontal?
(b) Why does the top of the film appear dark? ■

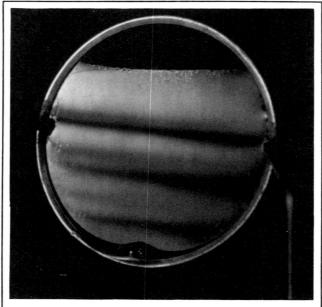

Figure 3.23

Q 3.47 Development question*

The *geometrical* path difference between the two waves reflected normally from opposite sides of a soap film is $2t$, where t is the thickness of the film. There is a slowing down of the waves in the liquid (refractive index n), and one wave undergoes a phase change on reflection which is equivalent to an extra path of $\lambda/2$. Therefore, the effective or *optical* path difference is $2nt + \lambda/2$.
(a) If the two waves interfere constructively to produce a strong reflected wave, complete the equation

$$2nt + \lambda/2 = \dots$$

(b) If λ_{max} is a wavelength which will be reflected strongly from a particular liquid film viewed normally, show that

$$\lambda_{max} = \frac{4nt}{2m - 1}$$

where m can be 1, 2, 3, etc.

If $n = 3/2$ and $t = 10^{-7}$ m, we can find the colour of the film, remembering that
$\lambda_{blue} = 4 \times 10^{-7}$ m, $\lambda_{yellow} = 6 \times 10^{-7}$ m, $\lambda_{red} = 7 \times 10^{-7}$ m.
(c) What is the colour of λ_{max} for $m = 1$ for this film thickness?
(d) What is the colour of λ_{max} reflected strongly for $m = 2$?

Values of $m = 3$, $m = 4$, $m = 5$ predict that u.v. wavelengths will be reflected strongly, so a film of thickness 10^{-7} m will look yellow.
(e) Predict the colour of films of thickness (i) 8×10^{-8} m and (ii) 2×10^{-7} m. ■

Questions on objectives

1 Explain the term *resolving power of an optical instrument* and state what determines its value. Which has the greater resolving power, the human eye (pupil diameter 2 mm) using light of wavelength 5.0×10^{-7} m or a radio telescope with a dish diameter of 77 m using radio waves of wavelength 21 cm?

(objectives 2 and 4)

2 Draw a diagram showing the experimental set up for observing single slit diffraction. Show on your diagram the intensity distribution of the light in the plane of observation.

(objective 4)

3 A glass sheet coated with opaque paint has many narrow slits ruled on it at regular spacings to form a grating. It is illuminated by a distant small monochromatic source and a series of bright lines are observed on looking into the grating. What will happen to the position and intensity of these lines if every other slit is blocked out?

(objective 5)

4 What is a pure spectrum? Outline the requirements for producing a pure spectrum. What are the advantages and disadvantages of a diffraction grating as compared with a prism for studying spectra?

(objective 8)

5 What are the conditions essential for the production of optical interference fringes? How are these conditions satisfied in the case of
(a) Young's fringes,
(b) thin film interference?

(objective 10)

6 Describe briefly an experiment to demonstrate that gases absorb strongly some of the radiations characteristic of their emission spectra.

(objective 9)

7 White light is reflected normally from a soap film of refractive index 4/3 and is then directed through the slit of a spectrometer to a diffraction grating at normal incidence. A dark band is observed in the first order spectrum. Explain this effect.

If the minimum intensity in the dark band occurs at 18° to the normal and the grating has 500 lines per mm, find the minimum thickness which the soap film could have at this point to fit the observed facts. Give one other possible answer for the thickness of the soap film.

(objectives 10 and 11)

4

Aim

The aim of this chapter is to develop a simple understanding of the nature of electromagnetic waves. You will compare the properties of different kinds of electromagnetic waves and find out how the wavelength affects these properties. You will observe the effects produced by passing plane polarised light beams through different media, develop hypotheses to account for these effects and learn how these properties have useful applications. The diffraction of X-rays by crystal structures will be studied.

Right. Jodrell Bank mark 1A radiotelescope.

Chapter 4

Objectives

When you have completed this chapter you should be able to:

1 Use the following scientific terms correctly: electromagnetic waves, the electromagnetic spectrum, X-ray diffraction, plane of vibration, plane-polarised light, partially polarised light, unpolarised light, polariser, crossed arrangement, analyser, Polaroid, double refraction, selective absorption, scattering, photo-elasticity, optical activity.

2 Outline briefly the nature of electromagnetic waves.

3 Describe the main types of radiations in the electromagnetic spectrum and outline the methods of production and detection and the properties of different radiations in the electromagnetic spectrum.

4 Outline the methods for producing plane-polarised light by reflection and by selective absorption.

5 Describe applications of the use of plane-polarised light, including the polarimeter and the strain gauge.

6 Describe qualitatively how the diffraction of X-rays is used to provide information about the structure of crystals.

7 EXTENSION
Use Bragg's Law in quantitative examples of X-ray diffraction.

8 EXTENSION
Derive a relationship between refractive index and polarising angle (Brewster's law).

Experiments in chapter 4

VW 17 Polarisation of microwaves
(½ hour)
VW 18 Polarising light waves
(¾ hour)
VW 19 Investigating stress
(¾ hour)
VW 20 A simple polarimeter
(¾ hour)

References

Bolton   Chapters 6, 7, 12
Duncan FWA   Chapter 8
Duncan MM   Chapter 1
Nelkon   Chapters 25, 27, 28
Millar   Chapters 27, 28
Whelan   Chapters 37, 39, 40

Study time: 1 week

4.1 Introduction

The light waves you have been studying in the last chapter are only one of the forms of radiation which we call electromagnetic waves. When we observe the spectrum of light from the sun we are dealing with only a very small part of its energy radiation spectrum. Most of the energy reaching the earth from the sun is invisible, but we are made aware of this invisible radiation by its effects. Our environment of animal and plant life depends on the continual radiation of the sun's wide spectrum, visible and invisible, of electromagnetic waves.

Figure 4.1 shows the full spectrum of electromagnetic waves, the sources of different kinds of radiation and the various detectors used. Electromagnetic waves share many general wave properties with other types of waves, but they also form a family of waves with properties which are particular to electromagnetic waves.

Q 4.1 Self-assessment question

(a) State three properties of electromagnetic waves which are shared with mechanical waves.
(b) State three particular properties of electromagnetic waves. (Figure 4.1 provides some clues, but make sure your answer applies to *all* e.m. waves.)
(c) State the one factor which distinguishes one kind of electromagnetic wave from another. ■

You have already examined convincing evidence that light is a wave, but it is difficult to visualise such a wave.

Can we talk of crests and troughs for a light wave? What is it, if anything, that is 'going up and down' in the wave? A clue is found by remembering that light waves are emitted when electrons move between energy levels and the absorption of light energy can produce a movement of electrons to new energy levels.

Q 4.2 Development question

What can exert a force on an electron? ■

The most obvious answers to this question are electric and magnetic fields. So a possible wave model for light is that it is an 'electric field wave'. Equally possible is 'a magnetic field wave'. Fortunately, we don't have to choose between these: it turns out to be both.

4.2 The nature of electromagnetic waves

Let us discover why the name *electromagnetic* is appropriate for the family of waves which includes light waves.

Consider first what happens in a changing magnetic field. If a magnet is moved near a coil, we can detect an induced current in the coil. A current cannot flow unless there is an electric field set up to move charge around the wire and the conventional current direction (the direction in which positive charge may flow) indicates the direction of the electric field. This field is produced by the moving magnet even if the coil is not there (figure 4.2). Therefore *a changing magnetic field produces a changing electric field at right angles to the direction in which the magnetic field changes.*

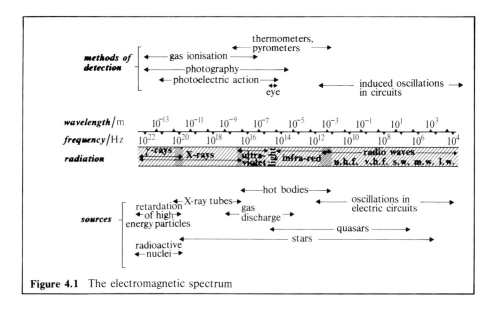

Figure 4.1 The electromagnetic spectrum

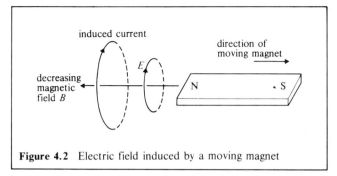

Figure 4.2 Electric field induced by a moving magnet

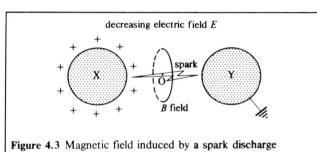

Figure 4.3 Magnetic field induced by a spark discharge

Now consider the changing electric field produced when a positively charged sphere X (figure 4.3) is discharged to an earthed sphere Y by a spark.

Q 4.3 Development question*

(a) What is the direction of the electric field at point O, between X and Y? Is it an increasing or a decreasing field?

(b) As the charge flows between X and Y, the electric field decreases and also a magnetic field B is produced around the charge flow. Describe the direction of the B-field (i) as viewed from X, (ii) in relation to the E-field.■

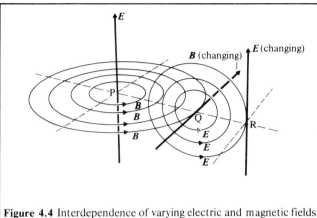

Figure 4.4 Interdependence of varying electric and magnetic fields

We can say that *a changing electric field produces a magnetic field which is perpendicular to the direction in which the electric field changes.*

Now suppose there is a *variable vertical electric field* at point P (see figure 4.4). This will produce a *horizontal magnetic field* around P. At a point Q some distance from P there is a *varying magnetic field.*

Q 4.4 Development question*

(a) Is the B-field at Q horizontal or vertical?

(b) The varying B-field at Q produces a varying electric field around Q. In what plane is the electric field around Q?

(c) What is the direction of the changing electric field at R?■

So it has been shown that a changing vertical electric field at P will result in a changing vertical field at R. There is, however, a time lag between the change in the

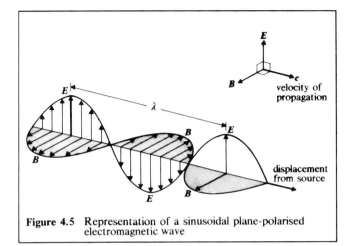

Figure 4.5 Representation of a sinusoidal plane-polarised electromagnetic wave

field at P and the resulting effect at R. If the electric field at one point varies periodically, then the electric field at a distant point will also vary periodically, but a little later in time. The result is the propagation of a wave, and we have a good analogy in the setting up of waves on the surface of water by a vibrating dipper. After a time lapse, the water surface some distance away from the dipper vibrates as a wave is propagated. Of course, the varying magnetic field at P will also produce, after a time lapse, a varying magnetic field at R. Changing electric and magnetic fields travel together from the source and an electromagnetic wave is propagated. Figure 4.5 represents an e.m. wave in which E and B-fields vary sinusoidally.

Note: An electromagnetic wave is the movement through space of a varying electric field accompanied by a varying magnetic field and each changing field is perpendicular to the direction of propagation of the wave. Electromagnetic waves are thus *transverse* waves.

The principles discussed above of the interdependence of electric and magnetic fields were the assumptions on which James Clerk Maxwell based his mathematical theory (published in 1873) that electrical disturbances with associated magnetic changes are propagated in space with a speed of $1/\sqrt{\epsilon_0 \mu_0}$ where ϵ_0 and μ_0 are the permittivity and permeability of free space respectively (see the Unit *Forces and fields*).

The surprising fact emerged that this velocity was very close to the velocity of light measured by Fizeau in 1849. The conclusion Maxwell came to was that light itself was an electromagnetic disturbance in the form of waves and that other similar radiations must exist. One of these 'other radiations' was discovered in 1888, when Heinrich Hertz produced radio waves using a spark transmitter. This development of knowledge about electromagnetic waves emphasises the important complementary roles of theoretical and experimental scientists.

Hertz's spark transmitter (figure 4.6a) is essentially a capacitor which is charged up by an induction coil. Charging of the capacitor continues until the p.d. across the spark gap produces a breakdown potential gradient ($300\ \text{V mm}^{-1}$) and a spark is produced. The spark oscillates very rapidly in the narrow ionised air gap (see figure 4.6b) producing an oscillating electric field E until the ions are collected and charging up starts again.

Hertz wrote: 'I tried whether the observed electrical disturbances did not manifest effects of corresponding magnitude in neighbouring conductors. I therefore bent some copper wire into the form of rectangular circuits,

about 10-20 cm in the side, and containing only very short spark-gaps . . . when the rectangle was brought sufficiently near, a stream of sparks in it always accompanied the discharges of the induction coil . . .'

The energy detected by the spark gap had been carried by an electromagnetic wave from the transmitter.

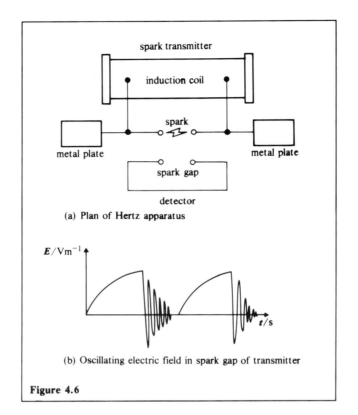

(a) Plan of Hertz apparatus

(b) Oscillating electric field in spark gap of transmitter

Figure 4.6

Unpolarised and plane-polarised waves

Figure 4.5 represents an electromagnetic wave in which the plane containing the electric vector is fixed. It is therefore described as a *plane-polarised wave*. Such a wave can be represented by simple diagrams (figure 4.7), which each indicate the plane containing the electric vector and the direction of propagation (called the *plane of vibration*). The arrows show the direction of the varying electrical field vector E. The magnetic field direction is not indicated, since we can always assume its presence and direction and it is the electric field which is more involved in the interaction between electromagnetic waves and atoms.

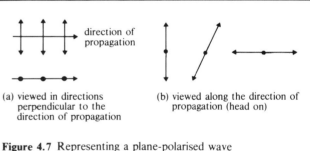

(a) viewed in directions perpendicular to the direction of propagation

(b) viewed along the direction of propagation (head on)

Figure 4.7 Representing a plane-polarised wave

Q 4.5 Self-assessment question
Draw a diagram to represent the plane-polarised waves travelling from transmitter to detector in Hertz's experiment (figure 4.6)
(a) viewed from above, and
(b) viewed from a point near a metal plate (side view). ∎

Many electromagnetic waves are propagated as a group of numerous individual wave pulses travelling together. For example, light is emitted as the result of the acceleration of electrons in many atoms of the source and these accelerations occur at random producing a light beam made up of many pulses, each pulse having a different plane of vibration for its electric vector field. We can represent this kind of radiation diagrammatically as shown in figure 4.8. An electromagnetic wave whose electric field vectors vary randomly with time in both magnitude and direction is an *unpolarised* wave.

Each of the electric vectors shown in figure 4.8 can be resolved into two component vibrations in planes at right angles to each other. By adding together all these components of random vibrations and averaging with time, an unpolarised wave can be considered as equivalent to a pair of superposed plane-polarised waves with the same average amplitude (but with a random phase difference). Thus figure 4.9 shows ways of representing an unpolarised wave showing the two *major equal components* of E at right angles.

If one of these major component electric vibrations can be removed, an unpolarised wave can be converted into a plane-polarised wave with all the electric field vibrations in one plane, the plane of vibration.

If one of the major components of an unpolarised wave is not removed completely but reduced in magnitude, the wave is described as a *partially polarised* wave.

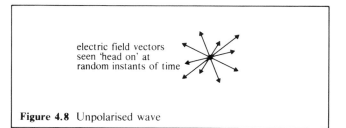

Figure 4.8 Unpolarised wave

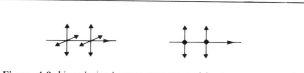

Figure 4.9 Unpolarised wave represented by two superposed component plane-polarised waves

E **Experiment VW 17**
Polarisation of microwaves
In this experiment you will investigate how the polarisation of 3 cm radio waves can be analysed and changed.

Q **4.6 Development question***
Figure 4.10 shows a modern version of Hertz's apparatus for transmitting and detecting radio waves. A high frequency varying electric field applied across a narrow gap between brass rods at T will produce a plane-polarised radio wave. This is called a transmitting dipole. The travelling electric and magnetic fields create a varying electric field between the receiver rods at R, which produces oscillations in the receiver circuit.

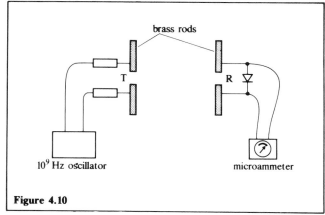

Figure 4.10

(a) In which plane will the electric field of this wave be vibrating? Give a reason for your answer.
(b) What is the wavelength of these radio waves?
(c) What will happen if the receiver aerial is turned through 90° about an axis TR so that the receiver dipole is horizontal?
(d) When the transmitter dipole is vertical, as shown, and the receiver dipole is horizontal, as in part (c), a metal rod is placed between them with its axis perpendicular to line TR and inclined at 45° to the vertical. Detectable waves are now produced in the receiver. Suggest an explanation.
(e) What is the function of the diode? Explain how it makes possible the detection of the waves.■

4.3 Polarisation of light waves

The human eye cannot distinguish between plane-polarised and unpolarised light. There is evidence that some other living things (e.g., bees) can detect the polarisation of light—a fact which provides an explanation of the guidance system of bees. If we are to detect and analyse the polarisation of light waves, we need the help of analysers like Polaroid.

Polaroid is made up of long chain molecules to which iodine atoms are attached. The presence of iodine allows electrons to move along the chains. The chains are aligned in one direction so that they behave like a fine grille of conducting wires which prevent transmission of any light with the electric field E vibrating parallel to the long chains (figure 4.11). (In experiment VW 17 you observed how a grille of metal wires could absorb microwaves whose plane of vibration was parallel to the wires.) If the electric field vibrates across the chains, light is transmitted.

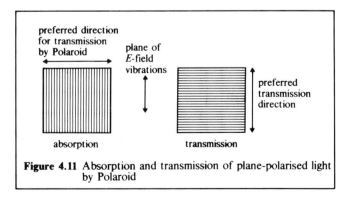

Figure 4.11 Absorption and transmission of plane-polarised light by Polaroid

Experiment VW 18
Polarising light waves

In this experiment, plane-polarised light is produced by different methods and analysed by Polaroid to obtain evidence that light is a transverse wave.

Figure 4.12 shows a sheet of Polaroid used as a *polariser* (converting unpolarised light into plane-polarised light). The figure also shows how a second Polaroid can be used as an *analyser* to locate the plane of polarisation. As the analysing Polaroid is rotated, the transmitted light changes from maximum to zero (this is true for 'ideal' Polaroid but, in practice, there is no complete extinction although high quality Polaroid comes close to the ideal). When the Polaroids are *crossed,* their preferred directions for transmission are at right angles.

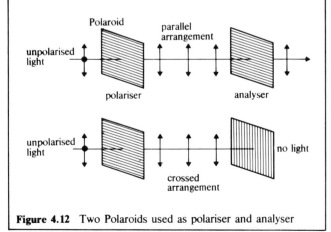

Figure 4.12 Two Polaroids used as polariser and analyser

Q 4.7 Study question*

A piece of Polaroid which is being used as an analyser is rotated through an angle θ from the parallel position (shown in figure 4.12). Sketch the face of the Polaroid marking in the angle θ and the direction of the E-field vibrations. Hence show that the transmitted light intensity is proportional to $\cos^2 \theta$. ∎

Q 4.8 Self-assessment question

The dazzling effect of the headlights of approaching traffic is a hazard for night drivers. It has been suggested that the use of Polaroid filters for headlights and driving glasses could overcome the hazard. Can you suggest how the Polaroid can be arranged so that a driver sees his own headlight beam but is not dazzled by other cars?∎

Double refraction

When light falls on certain crystals (e.g., calcite, quartz) two refracted beams are produced travelling at different speeds in the crystal. It is found that the two beams are each plane-polarised with electric fields vibrating at right angles. Some of these doubly refracting crystals absorb the energy of one of these beams and so transmit plane-polarised light. The crystals used in making Polaroid have a similar ability of selectively absorbing one component of light.

Some transparent materials exhibit double refraction when subjected to stress and their use in stress analysis is discussed in section 4.4.

Q 4.9 Study question

You can observe double refraction by placing a large calcite crystal on a page of a book. How could you test whether the two beams are each plane-polarised? Obtain the necessary apparatus and check your suggestion.■

Polarisation by reflection

When unpolarised light is reflected from dielectrics (insulators) like glass and water, the reflected light is always partially polarised. Light with the electric vector parallel to the reflecting surface is reflected most strongly.

If reflected and refracted beams make an angle of 90° with each other, the reflected wave will be plane-polarised (see figure 4.13). This condition occurs at a particular angle of incidence for two given media and a particular wavelength, and this angle is called the polarising angle.

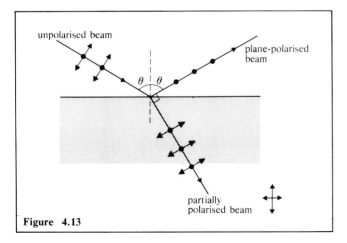

Figure 4.13

Q 4.10 Self-assessment question

(a) How can Polaroid glasses help to reduce the glare due to reflection of light from the ground?
(b) Why can you see fish in a river better with Polaroid glasses than without?■

SYLLABUS EXTENSION

Q 4.11 Study question

Using figure 4.13, define the polarising angle θ and deduce a relationship between the refractive index and the polarising angle. Calculate the polarising angle for glass ($n = 1.5$).■

Q 4.12 Self-assessment question

What will happen to a beam of unpolarised light as it is transmitted through a series of glass plates arranged so that the light is incident at the polarising angle?■

Polarising by scattering

Light waves can only consist of transverse oscillations, and so when an unpolarised wave meets a scattering centre (see figure 4.14) the light scattered through 90° can only have a vibrating E-field in the direction of *one* of the major component E-vectors of the original unpolarised beam; vibrations in the direction of the other component of the unpolarised beam would constitute a longitudinal light wave, which is an impossibility. Thus light scattered through 90° is plane-polarised.

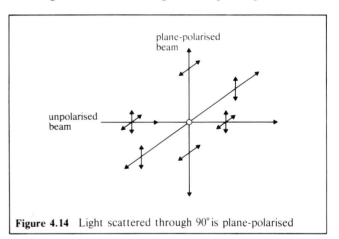

Figure 4.14 Light scattered through 90° is plane-polarised

Q 4.13 Self-assessment question

Describe how you would obtain evidence from analysis of the light scattered in the atmosphere to support the view that light is a transverse wave? Try out your suggestion.■

Q 4.14 Self-assessment question

Is the light from a half moon plane-polarised? Give a reason for your answer.■

4.4 Uses of polarised light

The analysis of polarised light provides a versatile tool for chemists, geologists and engineers in studying optically active solutions, minerals and materials under stress.

The experiments in this section provide an opportunity to study two important applications of polarised light, and an explanation of the relevant properties is provided in the text.

Photo-elasticity

E **Experiment VW 19**
Investigating stress
Polarised light is used to investigate stress in transparent materials.

Glass, perspex, polythene and some other plastics become doubly refracting when subjected to stress. In the unstressed material (e.g. perspex) light of a particular wavelength travels at a fixed speed. In stressed perspex, a plane-polarised incident beam will produce two refracted beams plane-polarised in different planes, one travelling at the unstressed speed and the other travelling more slowly. The wavelength of the light and the degree of stress determine the speed difference and the resulting phase difference between the two beams. Superposition effects seen when the specimen is viewed through crossed Polaroids depend on the phase difference produced and show dark fringes through lines of equal stress. In white light, coloured fringes are seen. The concentration of fringes can be used to measure the stress. Photoelasticity is used to analyse stress patterns in plastic models of various structures, when loaded, to inform engineers about the areas of stress concentration in the actual large-scale structures.

Optical activity

E **Experiment VW 20**
A simple polarimeter
Optical activity in sugar solution is observed and the factors on which it depends are investigated.

Certain crystals (e.g. quartz) and liquids (e.g. sugar solution) rotate the plane of vibration of a plane-polarised light wave which passes through them. These substances are called *optically active*. The amount of rotation depends on the concentration of an optically active solution and the length of the light path in the liquid.

Quartz and sodium chlorate crystals, even if only a few mm thick, will rotate the plane of polarisation many degrees. However, sodium chlorate in solution is not optically active, suggesting that the rotating or twisting property in this case depends on the structure of the crystal form. Many organic liquids (e.g. sugar solution) show optical activity which suggests that, in this case, the molecular structure itself is responsible for providing this rotating property.

Background reading
The ambidextrous universe, by M. Gardner, Penguin, 1967 (out of print).

AV **VW 10 Slideset**
Uses of polarised light
The slides show how polarised light can be used to investigate the structure of materials, and the stress patterns produced by loading a system.

4.5 The electromagnetic spectrum

All the recorded properties of different electromagnetic waves can be explained using the same basic physics, provided we make adjustments for differences in frequency. Frequency has two effects:

1 The size of the packets of energy in which the radiation is emitted depends on frequency, and the higher frequency radiations are emitted in larger energy packets. The fact is discussed fully in the Unit *Electrons and the nucleus*. It provides an explanation of why X-rays are more penetrating than light in metals and can ionise gases, and why a faint beam of light can affect a photographic plate whilst the powerful energy emission of a radio station produces no effect on a film.

2 Frequency (with speed) also determines wavelength, and the properties of waves depend on the comparative sizes of the wavelength and interacting matter. This means that a mountain is the same kind of obstacle to a long radio wave as a pinhead is to a wave of light.

It is important to note that there are no very precise boundaries between different types of waves, and some ranges overlap. Properties will obviously vary within a particular named range (e.g. between long and short infra-red), but there will be no abrupt change in properties between two different types of wave which have similar frequencies.

Waves of wavelength 10^{-10} m have exactly the same properties whether we call them X-rays, because they are produced by slowing down electrons, or gamma rays because they come from an excited nucleus. Fences around missile warning radar stations prevent cattle being cooked prematurely, though they may end up eventually as steak cooked in a microwave oven! This reminds us of the fact that infra-red waves and micro-waves used in radar both share similar heating properties.

Q 4.15 Self-assessment question
X-rays can ionise gases, light waves cannot. Explain this, and suggest (with a reason) which of the two types of radiation will be more penetrating in air. ∎

Sources and detectors
The *source* of wave energy emission moves from outside the atom to the nucleus as we move through the spectrum from long to short waves.

Radio waves are produced by oscillations of free electrons in matter; infra-red waves result from changes in the vibrational energy of molecules; visible and ultra-violet radiation are produced by energy changes in outer electrons in the atom; X-rays are produced by energy changes of inner orbital electrons and by the slowing down of fast electrons; γ-rays are produced by energy changes within the nucleus.

Detectors use any suitable property of the wave. Notice (figure 4.1) that ionisation, photography and heating effects are all used for a wide range of radiation. Light waves probably have the largest selection of detectors and, of course, include one—the eye—which is unique.

Q 4.16 Study question
Study figure 4.1 and any references in your books to the electromagnetic spectrum.
(a) Make a list of the different types of radiation in this spectrum in order of wavelength and for each type name one source and one kind of detector.
(b) List any properties which are used for detecting more than one kind of radiation, saying which kinds are detected in this common way. ∎

Reflection, refraction, transmission
Media transparent to one wave are opaque to others. Glass is not transparent for most ultra-violet and infra-red radiation, but quartz can transmit ultra-violet and rock salt can transmit infra-red. Special filters are used in photography to prevent ultra-violet rays reaching the film because the glass of the lens is transparent to some ultra-violet with wavelengths near to the visible region.

Q 4.17 Study question
Write a brief description of an ultra-violet spectroscope, indicating the materials used for prism, lenses, and detector. ∎

Q 4.18 Self-assessment question
What kind of grating is suitable for producing an infra-red spectrum (glass is not transparent to infra-red)? Will it be finer or coarser than a grating for light? ∎

Q 4.19 Self-assessment question
Which property of waves is used for the location and guidance of ships and aircraft? What kind of waves are used? ∎

Read the following description of an application for e.m. waves then answer question 4.20.

Partially deaf children are able to benefit from a new development in hearing aids designed for use in schools. Audio frequency signals are carried by electromagnetic waves of frequencies between 200 and 280 GHz and the hearing aid worn by a child consists of a small receiver carried on the chest and headphones. The electromagnetic waves are radiated into the classroom from a transmitter in the teacher's desk and also from four transmitters mounted in each corner of the room. The child's receiver is designed to give good reception in any position in the room. Stereo audio signals are used so that the separate channels can be set at the receiver to cater for each child's particular disability. The advantage of using these particular carrier waves is that interference between adjacent classrooms is impossible. In more conventional systems for the hard of hearing in schools, such interference can be a severe problem.

Q 4.20 Self-assessment question
(a) What name is given to this frequency range of electromagnetic radiation (see figure 4.1)?
(b) What property of these waves, not possessed by radio waves, makes interference impossible between classrooms? ∎

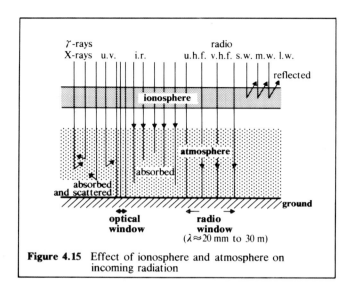

Figure 4.15 Effect of ionosphere and atmosphere on incoming radiation

Figure 4.15 shows how radiation from space is affected by the earth's atmosphere and the ion layer above it. It shows that there are only two windows (frequency ranges) open to receive light and very short radio waves. The upper atmosphere (ionosphere) is opaque to other radio frequencies.

In fact, long distance radio reception depends upon the reflection of radio waves from a layer of charged particles high in the ionosphere.

Q 4.21 Self-assessment question

Suggest suitable wavelengths for radio communication between London and Australia using
(a) a communications satellite system,
(b) ionospheric reflection. ■

Q 4.22 Self-assessment question

A radio receiver 150 km from a short-wave transmitter (broadcasting 30 m waves) receives two waves which are superposed at the receiver. One wave is diffracted around the earth's surface (the ground wave) and one is reflected from the ionosphere (the sky wave). Explain how continual changes in the ionospheric layer can produce fading (varying strength) reception at the receiver. Explain why the reception could be better at much greater distances from the transmitter. ■

Scattering

Light waves are scattered by gas molecules and tiny particles (smoke or dust). When a light wave impinges on an atom or molecule, the vibrating E-field interacts with the electrons producing a forced oscillation of the whole molecule which therefore absorbs some of the wave energy. The vibrating molecule will re-radiate energy in all directions, and this effect is known as *scattering*. The natural frequency of a typical vibrating molecule is in the ultra-violet region. If the incident light frequency is near to that of ultra-violet, the forced vibrations will be close to resonance and so a lot of energy will be absorbed and re-radiated (scattered). Longer wavelengths of light will produce less scattering; in fact, the degree of scattering is proportional to the fourth power of the frequency.

Particles of larger size (e.g. smoke particles) also produce scattering which is partly a diffraction effect and partly a reflection of waves. If the particles are smaller than the wavelength of light, long visible waves will be affected very little but the short waves will behave as though the particles were big obstacles and, as a result, short waves will be scattered more than long waves. If the particles are bigger than the wavelength of red light, then all visible waves treat the particles as big obstacles and all wavelengths are scattered significantly. The degree of scattering is independent of wavelength.

Q 4.23 Self-assessment question

(a) Give a reason why tobacco smoke appears blue but the 'steam' from a kettle is white.
(b) Why is the sky blue? What does an astronaut observe about the colour of the sun and sky as he moves up through the atmosphere?
(c) A camera using a film which is sensitive to infra-red rays can take a picture through a mist. Explain briefly why this is so. ■

Interference and diffraction

Consider now the importance of diffraction and interference effects on the transmission and reception of radio and television signals.

Q 4.24 Self-assessment question

People living near to an airport flight-path may get 'pulsing' of the television signal. With the help of figure 4.16, explain the cause of this 'pulsing' and describe what will be observed on the television screen. ■

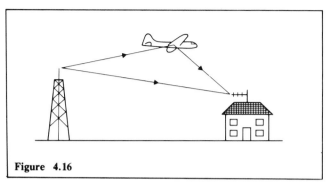

Figure 4.16

Q 4.25 Study question

Try to investigate the interference of v.h.f. radio or TV waves due to reflection from a metal sheet or large metal fence (tennis court fencing). The published table of v.h.f. radio transmitters will tell you in which direction the waves reach you.

Place the portable v.h.f. radio between the station and the reflector (figure 4.17) and move it slowly perpendicular to the reflector. The rod aerial can be used, or, better still, a special v.h.f. aerial. The best sets have circuits designed to keep the output volume constant, so a cheap radio is more suitable for this experiment and should be tuned slightly 'off station'. You can try the effect with u.h.f. television signals by moving an aerial perpendicular to a metal plate.

Use the method to obtain a measurement of the wavelength of the radio waves and compare this with the calibrated wavelength or frequency on your dial.■

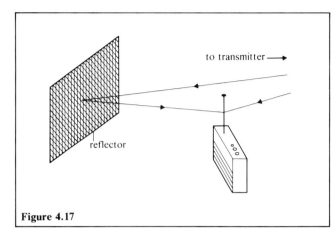

Figure 4.17

The size of the shadow produced by an obstacle depends on the relative sizes of obstacle and wavelength. If an obstacle is a similar size to the wavelength, then diffraction effects produce hardly any shadow.

We are much more aware of the spreading due to diffraction of long waves than that of short waves, for which diffraction effects are much less obvious. Indeed, we think of light travelling in straight lines, compared with long waves (like radio or sound waves) which are more obviously diffracted.

Q 4.26 Self-assessment question

What kind of radio waves would you think most suitable for transmitting sound radio programmes to a valley in the mountains? In such locations TV signals cannot be received at all and the signal is 'piped' from an aerial on the hilltop. Why does TV transmission call for a different solution?■

Q 4.27 Self-assessment question

Many telephone calls are now carried by radio waves. Very short wavelength waves (microwaves) have to be used because these waves can carry many more simultaneous messages than long radio waves. There are, however, problems to be overcome in transmitting microwaves. What are these particular problems and how are they overcome to provide a nationwide radio-telephone system?■

The next question will give you an opportunity to summarise your comparative study of e.m. waves.

Q 4.28 Study question

Give, for each of the seven named ranges of e.m. waves: γ-rays, X-rays, ultra-violet, visible, infra-red, microwave and radio,
(a) any characteristic properties which distinguish one range from another,
(b) applications in each particular range.■

X-ray diffraction

Q 4.29 Self-assessment question

What is the approximate wavelength of X-rays (see figure 4.1)? What fraction is this of the wavelength of light (in powers of 10)? If a grating for diffraction of light has 100 lines per cm, how many lines per cm are appropriate for an X-ray diffraction grating?■

When X-rays fall on a crystal structure, most rays pass straight through but some are scattered by the atoms or, to be more precise, by the distribution of electrons around each atom.

Von Laue first suggested, in 1912, that if the regular spacing of atoms in a crystal is of the same order as the wavelength of X-rays a crystal should act as a three-dimensional diffraction grating. Figure 4.18 shows the diffraction pattern (Laue pattern) produced on a photographic plate by sending non-monochromatic X-rays through a crystal using the method shown in the figure. This experiment by Laue and his colleagues provided convincing evidence that X-rays are waves.

In experiment MP 3 (in the Unit *Material properties*) you observed diffraction patterns produced when light waves are diffracted by different arrangements of regularly and irregularly spaced dots. The diffraction pattern obtained was determined by the arrangement of dots. The particular Laue pattern produced using a crystal as a transmission diffraction grating is determined by the crystal structure, but its analysis proved very difficult. Sir William Bragg and his son Sir Lawrence Bragg developed a simpler technique for crystal analysis, using

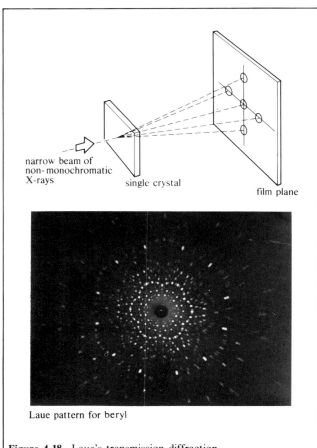

narrow beam of non-monochromatic X-rays   single crystal   film plane

Laue pattern for beryl

Figure 4.18 Laue's transmission diffraction

the crystal as a reflection grating. Sir Lawrence Bragg wrote, in an article on the history of X-ray analysis:

> At the start, my father was far more interested in spectra than in crystal structure. But it soon became apparent that the X-ray spectrometer which he had devised was a far more powerful way of analysing crystal structures than the laborious and indirect method of the Laue photograph. For instance, I had been trying to discover the structure of diamond from its Laue pictures with no success. My father's measurements with the spectrometer solved it immediately; I think it was the diamond structure which first brought home to the scientific world the importance and power of the new method.

In the same article, Bragg outlined the nature of the problem which X-ray analysis attempts to solve:

> The object is to get as accurate a map as possible of the positions of the atoms in a structure. A crystal structure lends itself to the analysis of the diffraction phenomena, because the units of pattern are regularly arranged and diffract in an identical way, but in general the crystal is only a means to an end and 'X-ray analysis of atomic arrangement' is a more appropriate title than 'X-ray analysis of crystals'. For inorganic substances, such as the minerals, the crystalline structure is an essential feature, because the pattern is a continuous one with no molecular boundaries. But in the vast field of the complex organic compounds, the crystalline structure is of quite secondary importance. The arrangement of atoms in the organic molecule is the object of the research.

SYLLABUS EXTENSION

Bragg's law

If a wall is covered with patterned wallpaper, a periodic repetition of the unit pattern is produced in two dimensions. Every crystal structure may be regarded as built up by the three-dimensional periodic repetition of identical units (unit cells). The unit cell may be a single atom or a group of ions (for example, the unit cell of sodium chloride contains four sodium ions and four chlorine ions). Unit cells were identified in models of metal structures in experiment MP 4 (Unit *Material properties*). Unit cells are the fundamental diffracting units (scattering centres) in a crystal and in any crystal all these unit cells can be contained within a set of parallel equally-spaced planes (Bragg planes). Figure 4.19 shows, in cross-section, several sets of Bragg planes in a simple crystal structure.

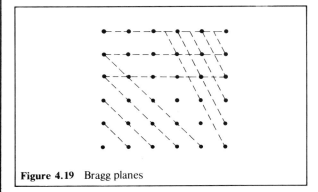

Figure 4.19 Bragg planes

Q **4.30 Development question***
Consider the scattering of X-rays from a single Bragg plane. The 'unit cells' A, B and C, figure 4.20, act as scattering centres (that is, they act as secondary sources of X-ray wavelets).
(a) Use Huygen's construction to find the new scattered wave front at the instant when X-rays reach D. (The path length is the same whether the wave energy travels *via* A, B or C.)
(b) What is the direction of the scattered wave front?

One plane of scattering centres has produced a weak 'reflected' beam, since the scattered wavelets superpose constructively in a direction for which the scattered wave front and incident wave front make the same angle with the crystal plane. This 'reflection' effect occurs whatever the value of θ.

Now consider X-rays scattered from successive Bragg planes. In figure 4.21, BE and BG are drawn parallel to the incident and scattered wave fronts, so the path difference between rays 1 and 2 is (EF + FG).
(c) Write down an expression for the path difference between rays 1 and 2 in terms of θ and d.
(d) What is the path difference between rays 2 and 3?
(e) What condition must be satisfied if rays 1 and 2, or 2 and 3, are to be in phase when they reach a distant detector?
(f) What will be the effect at a distant detector of scattering at other equally-spaced Bragg planes?
(g) Write down the condition for there to be a maximum diffracted beam at angle θ.
(h) Is the crystal acting as (i) a mirror, (ii) a transmission diffraction grating, or (iii) a reflection diffraction grating?■

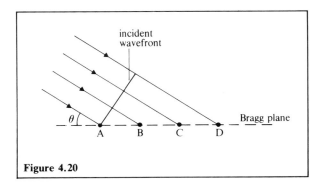

Figure 4.20

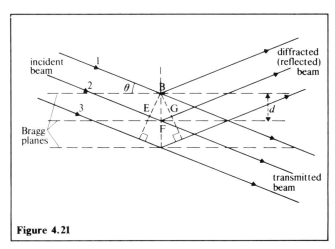

Figure 4.21

In an X-ray spectrometer, essentially mono-chromatic X-radiation of known wavelength is diffracted from a crystal. The crystal is rotated and the strong 'reflected' X-ray beams are detected for different values of θ (the glancing angle).

Q 4.31 Self-assessment question

Figure 4.22 shows a microwave analogue of an X-ray spectrometer. The microwaves are reflected from the set of polystyrene tiles on a rotating turntable and the receiver is moved to locate positions where a strong signal is received. If the tile spacing is 4 cm and the wavelength of the microwaves is 3 cm, state three positions of the receiver at which a strong signal will be received. ∎

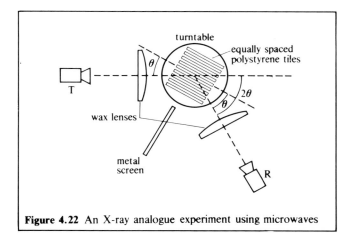

Figure 4.22 An X-ray analogue experiment using microwaves

AV VW 11 Film loop X-ray diffraction

The effect of the diffraction of monochromatic X-rays by a single crystal and by a powder specimen can be observed.

AV VW 12 Filmstrip Materials and structure

These slides show ways of obtaining X-ray diffraction patterns from a single crystal, and from a powder of tiny crystals, and the patterns which are obtained.

The relationship derived in question 4.30, known as Bragg's law, is important in helping scientists to plot the structural plan of atoms from knowledge of X-ray wavelengths. Also, diffraction effects from known crystal structures can provide information about the *X-ray spectra* of different sources.

Q 4.32 Self-assessment question

Figure 4.23 is the graph obtained when X-rays are 'reflected' from a crystal of rock salt.
(a) If the X-rays are diffracted from a set of planes in the rock salt with spacing 2.18×10^{-10} m, calculate the wavelength of the X-rays which produced the three peaks A, B and C at 9.9°, 11.6° and 13.6° respectively.
(b) What caused the peaks D, E, F and G, H, I?
(c) The same X-rays were directed at an unkown sample and the three first order peaks occurred at angles of 7.2°, 8.4° and 9.8°. Calculate the atomic spacing of the Bragg planes in this case. ∎

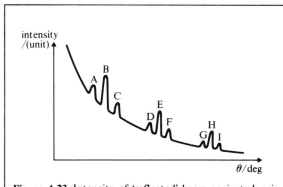

Figure 4.23 Intensity of 'reflected' beam against glancing angle for X-rays

Measurement of the frequencies of the characteristic lines in the X-ray spectra emitted by different sources provided the vital clue in the development of the idea of atomic number. This significant work is discussed fully in the Unit *Electrons and the nucleus.*

Comprehension exercise

Spectroscopy

Consider three important but very different ways in which the spectra of electromagnetic waves provide valuable information.

1 Emission spectra in steel working

At a critical moment in the manufacture of steel, the prepared melt has to be analysed before it is poured into moulds and its composition must be modified if necessary. Very speedy analysis is required. A tiny sample is poured into a mould, cooled, and a slice is cut and polished and placed in a spark chamber (figure 4.24). The spark source produces radiation which includes the characteristic ultra-violet emission of the elements in the disc. This radiation is dispersed by two fluorite prisms and produces a spectrum along a curved focal surface. Slits are positioned so that the particular wavelengths of radiation which are required for the steelmaker's analysis are passed through the slits and reflected into a set of photomultiplier tubes (which produce an electron current when ultra-violet is incident on them). The signals from the photomultiplier are fed into a computer which prints out the percentage composition of the steel based on information given to it about the intensity of the characteristic ultra-violet emissions of different elements. Six minutes after pouring the sample, the decision can be taken whether to pour or modify the melt.

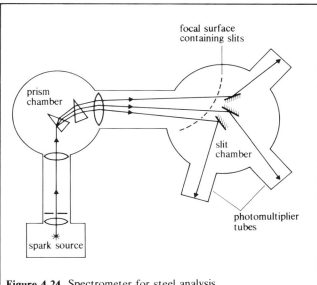

Figure 4.24 Spectrometer for steel analysis

2 Molecular absorption spectra

Figure 4.25 lists the components required to produce molecular absorption spectra in different parts of the e.m. spectrum. When ultra-violet or visible radiation is absorbed by a complex molecule, it is used to change the energy of the electrons and also to change the vibration and rotation of the whole molecule (see chapter 1 on resonance). This explains why molecular spectra are complex band spectra, in contrast to the simpler line spectra of atoms. When infra-red radiation is absorbed by molecules, the radiation can affect only changes in the rotational and vibrational energy of the whole molecule. If microwaves were used, with wavelengths of about 3 cm, molecules could only absorb energy which would affect their rotation. The measurement of the wavelengths at which molecules absorb different radiations (i.e., their

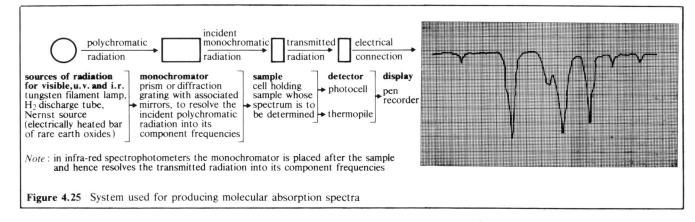

Figure 4.25 System used for producing molecular absorption spectra

absorption spectra) in different regions of the electromagnetic spectrum will provide a lot of information about the structure and grouping of atoms in a very complex molecule.

3 Flash photolysis

This is a method of studying fast chemical reactions. In 1967 Professor G. Porter and R. G. W. Norrish were awarded the Nobel Prize for Chemistry for their work in developing this method.

Some chemical reactions can be initiated by light energy, and in the flash photolysis method the reaction is triggered off by an intense light flash from the photoflash tube (figure 4.26). The progress of the rapid reaction taking place in the reaction tube is observed by sending light from a second flash tube (the spectroscopic flash) through the reaction vessel and into a spectrograph. By photographing the absorption spectrum at very rapid intervals, using the spectroscopic flash, information can be obtained about the progress of the reaction and the free radicals produced in the tube.

In the past few years, the ability to time-resolve molecular events in photochemistry has improved enormously. Until recently, the resolution of events by flash photolysis has been limited to a few microseconds. Now, through new techniques, flash photolysis may be applied to species lasting a few nanoseconds. These improvements depended on the introduction of the laser into photochemistry.

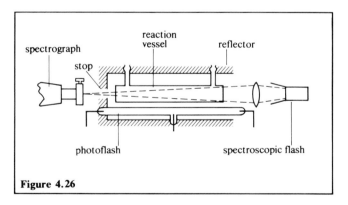

Figure 4.26

Questions

Emission spectra in steel making

1 Suggest reasons why *fluorite* prisms are used, and why *two*.

2 Why is the slit plate curved?

3 Why is the sample disc polished?

4 Why is it necessary to use the sample disc in a spark source instead of just heating it until it is white hot?

Molecular spectroscopy

5 Why are molecular spectra more complex than atomic spectra?

6 Choose from the lists in figure 4.25 a set of components suitable for obtaining an infra-red spectrogram.

7 Molecules only absorb energy from radiation of particular frequencies. Mention an analogous example of resonance occurring in sound or in the mechanical vibrations of a system.

Flash photolysis

8 Give two reasons why capacitors are needed in the circuits controlling the flash tubes.

9 Why are two flash tubes used? How do their functions differ?

10 The term *kinetic spectroscopy* is used for methods like this. Why is this term appropriate?

Questions on objectives

1 Light and X-rays are both said to be electromagnetic waves.
(a) What kind of experimental results suggest that both are waves?
(b) Mention any evidence that might suggest that light and X-rays are the same kind of radiation.
(c) What arguments, based on experimental results, can you give to suggest that they have very different wavelengths.

(objectives 2 and 3)

2 Explain what is meant by plane-polarised light. Describe one method of producing a plane-polarised beam. Why is it not possible to polarise sound waves?
(objective 4)

3 An analyser for a light beam is available. How would you use it to distinguish between
(a) partially polarised,
(b) completely plane-polarised,
(c) unpolarised light?
(objective 1)

4 Sketch a diagram showing how Polaroid sunglasses can be used to reduce glare
(a) from the surface of a river,
(b) from sunlight when the sun is vertically overhead.
Indicate on your sketch the direction in the Polaroid which transmits plane-polarised light.
(objective 4)

5 Give an account of two uses of polarised light.
(objective 5)

6 Suggest reasons for
(a) the blue of the sky,
(b) the red of the sunset,
(c) the white of the clouds.
(objective 3)

7 In a fine mist, clearer photographs of distant objects can be taken by infra-red film than by film sensitive only to visible light, yet when the fog is thick, neither film can be used. Explain.
(objective 3)

8 Compare the properties of X-rays and ultra-violet radiation.
(objective 3)

Experiment VW1   Motion of vibrating systems

Aim
The aim of this series of experiments is to find the properties common to some vibrating systems.

Apparatus
A number of vibrating systems should be available, for example:
- mass hanging on a spring
- ball on a curved track
- trolley between springs
- torsional pendulum
- simple pendulum
- loaded lath
- mercury in U-tube
- sand pendulum
- additional springs
- stop watch
- metre rule

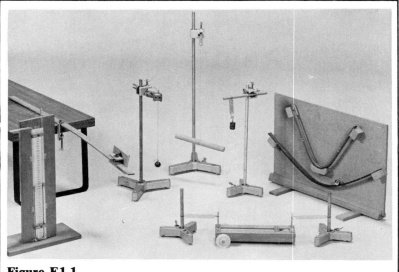

Figure E1.1

Periodic time and amplitude
1   This is an introductory experiment and you should just make a quick survey of several of the vibrating systems shown in figure E1.1 and figure 1.2 (chapter 1).

2   Find the time for a fixed number of vibrations for several systems. From your results, try to decide whether or not the periodic time depends upon the amplitude of the motion.
Note: The amplitude is the size of the maximum displacement from the equilibrium position.
The periodic time is the time of one complete vibration (i.e. a double swing).

Obtaining a time trace of the motion
1   Set up a sand pendulum as shown in figure E1.2a so that the sand falls in a gentle trickle on to the paper.

2   Set the pendulum swinging and pull the paper steadily across the floor or bench under the pendulum so that the dry sand makes a trace on the paper.

3   Describe the trace that you observe. What name does this shape suggest to you?

4   (Optional)
Use your ingenuity to obtain a time-trace for some of the other vibrating systems or oscillators.

Vibrations of a loaded spring
1   Attach a mass to a spring, which is supported by means of a clamp as shown in figure E1.2b.

2   Determine the periodic time by timing a counted number of vibrations.

3   Investigate the effect on the periodic time of:
(a) doubling the mass of the vibrating system (using the same spring)
(b) doubling and halving the stiffness of the vibrating system (using the original mass).
Note: Connecting two springs in series will halve the stiffness, whereas connecting them in parallel will double it. (Of course, you must have similar springs.)

4   What happens to the periodic time when the mass is doubled and the restoring force is halved?

The simple pendulum

Set up a simple pendulum as in figure E1.2c and determine its period of vibration by timing at least twenty-five vibrations.

Vary the mass and the amplitude of the vibration to find answers to the following questions.

a) Does the period depend on the mass of the bob?

b) Does the period depend on the amplitude of the swing?

Keep the mass of the pendulum bob and the starting amplitude constant, and obtain a series of values for the period T and the corresponding length l.

By plotting suitable graphs find a relationship between the period T and the length l.

Why is it an advantage to have as wide a range of values of l and T as possible? What can you say about the limiting case when l is zero?

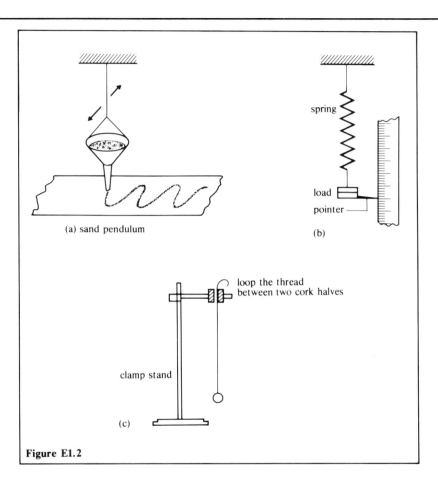

(a) sand pendulum

spring

load

pointer

(b)

loop the thread between two cork halves

clamp stand

(c)

Figure E1.2

Experiment VW2 Effect of damping on a vibrating system

Aim

The aim of this experiment is to find out how the amplitude of a vibrating system changes with time when damping forces are present.

Apparatus

- base holder
- strip of spring steel
- load to attach to steel
- card to provide damping
- pointer
- metre rule
- stop watch

1 Set up the apparatus as shown in figure E2.

Note: The position of the load and the dimensions of the card should be adjusted so that the system has a long period of vibration. This is to ensure that sufficient measurements of amplitude can be made before the motion ceases.

2 Displace the strip of steel to one side and record the initial amplitude a_0.

3 Release the strip and start the stop watch. Observe the motion of the strip and record the time and the maximum displacement after each consecutive vibration.

4 Plot a graph to show how the amplitude of the motion varies with time.

5 Explain the behaviour of the vibrating system. Does the graph show a simple mathematical pattern?

Hint: Does it take the same time to decay from its initial amplitude a_0 to an amplitude of $a_0/2$ as it does from $a_0/2$ to $a_0/4$? What name would you give to describe this type of decay?

Your graph shows a complex behaviour; not all damped oscillators follow a simple pattern.

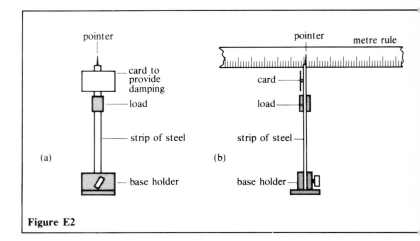

Figure E2

Experiment VW3 Barton's pendulums

Aim

The aim of this experiment is to observe what happens when a system is made to vibrate at some frequency other than its own natural frequency of vibration.

Apparatus

paper cone pendulums of varying length
pendulum with heavy bob
string and suitable support

1   Set up the apparatus as shown in figure E3.

2   Pull the driver pendulum to one side so that it vibrates in a direction perpendicular to the plane of the diagram.

3   Observe and describe what happens to the pendulums initially and after a period of time (e.g. 10-15 minutes).

4   What did you notice about the frequency and amplitude of the pendulums? Which pendulum had the largest amplitude? How did its effective length compare with the length of the driving pendulum?

5   Were all the pendulums in step, that is, did they all pass through the point of their maximum displacement (or the equilibrium position) at the same time? If not, what did you observe about the way in which the driver pendulum was vibrating compared to the pendulum with the largest amplitude? What was the approximate value of the phase difference and which was leading?

6   Investigate the effect of making the driven pendulums more massive, for example, by placing metal rings or washers on top of the paper cones, thus reducing the relative damping.

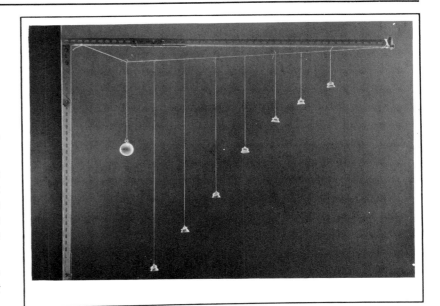

Experiment VW4 An investigation of resonance

Aim

The aim of this experiment is to investigate what happens when a system which can vibrate at a definite frequency is driven by another vibrating system whose frequency can be varied.

Apparatus

- hack-saw blade oscillator
- stop watch
- G-clamp
- metre rule
- postcard
- cork
- needle
- rubber band
- retort stand
- boss
- clamp

Arranging the vibrating system

1 Set up the apparatus as shown in figure E4. The pendulum is connected by a rubber band to a vertical hack-saw blade. The positions of the pendulum bob and the sliding mass can be adjusted to alter the natural frequencies of each of the two vibrators. The damping of the blade can be varied by turning the card so that it is at right angles to the direction of motion of the blade and by fitting cards of various sizes. The apparatus must be firmly clamped to the bench.

2 Adjust the position of the sliding mass until the natural frequency of the blade is approximately the same as that of the pendulum, when the bob is fixed half-way down the pendulum.
Note: When you are making these adjustments the two vibrating systems must *not* be coupled together.

3 Connect the two systems together by means of one or more rubber bands, adjust the bands until the coupled systems oscillate smoothly.

Undamped vibrations

1 Move the pendulum bob so that the pendulum has its lowest frequency. Start the pendulum oscillating and aim to keep its amplitude almost constant by tapping it at intervals.

2 Time a known number of oscillations and determine the frequency of the pendulum.

3 Observe the motion of the blade and try to find the answers to the following questions.
What is the frequency of the blade?
How does the amplitude of the blade vary? Give an explanation of its behaviour.
What is the approximate phase difference between the pendulum and the blade?

4 Repeat the experiment for different lengths of the pendulum and each time determine the frequency of the pendulum (the *driving*

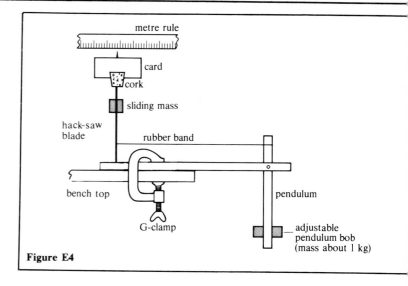

Figure E4

frequency), and the amplitude of the blade (the *driven* amplitude Estimate the phase difference.

5 Plot a graph of the driven amplitude (y-axis) against the drivir frequency (x-axis). The curve that you obtain is called a resonanc curve.

Damped vibrations

1 Damp the motion of the blade by turning the card so that it is a right angles to the direction of motion, repeat the experiment and pl a resonance curve for the damped motion.

2 What effect does damping have on the time taken for the drive oscillator to acquire a steady amplitude?

3 How does the curve differ from that obtained for the undampe blade?

Experiment VW5   Coupled pendulums

Aim

The aim of this experiment is to observe and explain what happens when two pendulums of equal mass are coupled together.

Apparatus

2 pendulums with heavy bobs string and suitable support

1   Set up the apparatus as shown in figure E5.

2   Initially allow one of the pendulums to swing in a plane perpendicular to the plane of the diagram.

3   Observe and describe what happens to the subsequent motion of the two pendulums.

4   Explain how the energy is transferred between the two oscillators.

5   What is the phase relationship between the two oscillators? (Are they in phase, exactly out of phase, or is there some other relationship?)

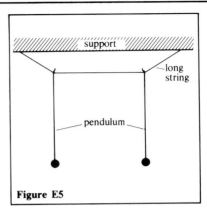

Figure E5

Experiment VW6　A study of a wave model

Aim

In this experiment a wave pulse is sent through a line of trolleys joined by springs. You will observe that the pulse speed depends on the mass of the trolleys and the tension in the connecting springs.

Apparatus

- 12 dynamics trolleys (or 6 trolleys and 6 one kilogram masses)
- 16 dowel rods
- 20 springs (steel, expendable)
- 20 springs, compression
- G-clamp
- stop watch

Transverse pulse

1　Arrange the six dynamics trolleys as shown in figure E6.1, with the trolleys spaced out so that the springs are in tension.

2　Move the free-end trolley from side to side to send a transverse pulse down the line of trolleys. Time the interval between the start of the pulse and the return of the reflected pulse. Repeat four more times and record your results. Find the average time.
Note:　Always move the trolley about the same point, i.e. keep the length of the trolley line constant so that the extension of each spring remains constant.

3　Investigate the effect of doubling the mass by attaching a second trolley to each trolley. (Use 1 kg masses if extra trolleys are not available.) Again record the time for 5 pulses and find the average.

4　Remove the extra trolleys (or 1 kg masses) and attach a second pair of springs between each trolley as shown in figure E6.2. Repeat steps 2 and 3.

Figure E6.1

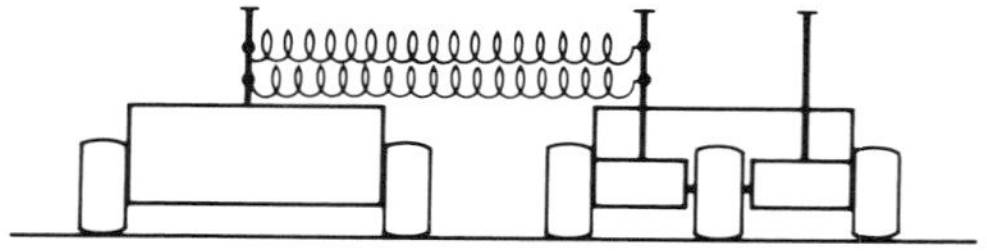

Figure E6.2

5　Calculate the pulse speed for each case.

6　What happens to the pulse speed when the mass of each trolley is doubled?
What happens to the pulse speed when the tension is doubled?
What can you say about the pulse speed when the mass and tension are both doubled at the same time?

7　Why is this a reasonable model for the propagation of a transverse wave in a string? What do the springs and trolleys represent?

Longitudinal pulse

1　Arrange the six trolleys as shown in figure E6.3. Each trolley is linked to the next one by means of a compression spring.

2　Send a compression pulse along the line of trolleys and calculate the speed of the pulse down the row of trolleys.

3　What happens to the speed of the pulse when the mass of each trolley is doubled?

4　Why is this a reasonable model for the propagation of a longitudinal wave in air? What do the springs and trolleys represent?

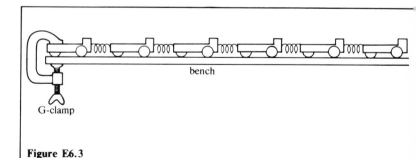

bench

G-clamp

Figure E6.3

Aim

To produce a stationary wave pattern on a string and investigate the effect of changing the driving frequency and tension in the string.

Apparatus

signal generator
vibrator
pulley
string

A stationary wave pattern

1   Attach a string, of uniform thickness and length approximately 150 cm, to one end of the vibrator, mounted so that its movement is vertical. Pass the other end of the string over a small pulley and attach a mass (e.g. 100 g) as shown in figure E7.1.

2   Connect the vibrator to the signal generator. Observe the amplitude of the string's transverse motion as the frequency is slowly increased and then decreased.

3   Find the lowest frequency that produces a point of maximum displacement at the mid-point of the string (i.e. one loop in the string). Record this frequency.
Note: You may need to adjust the tension in the string and/or the length of the string to obtain this pattern.

4   Keep the tension and length constant and find the lowest frequency that produces a stationary point at the midpoint of the string (i.e. two loops). Record this frequency.

5   Find a relationship between the number of loops n and frequency f, for the same values of T and l.

Relationship between T and f

1   Adjust the frequency to produce a pattern as shown in figure E7.2. Record the values of the tension T and frequency f.

2   Increase the tension (by adding an additional mass) and find the new frequency at which the string has the same mode of vibration. Record the values of T and f.

3   Repeat step 2 for at least three other values of tension.

4   Plot graphs which show the relationship between frequency and tension. Write down an equation which relates these quantities.
(*Hint*: It is difficult to interpret a curve but a straight line will indicate a relation more conclusively.)

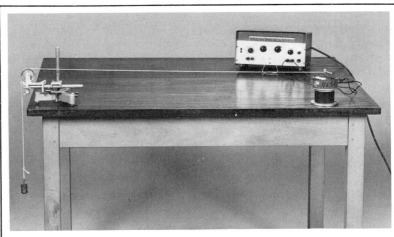

Figure E7.1

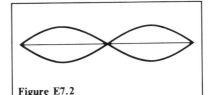

Figure E7.2

Experiment VW8   Stationary waves in an air column

Aim

To investigate how the air vibrates in a tube and measure the speed of sound in an air column.

Apparatus

- glass tube (1.0 m-1.5 m long)
- rubber bung
- loudspeaker, diameter 60 mm
- signal generator
- lycopodium powder or cork dust
- metre rule

1   Thoroughly clean and dry the glass tube and introduce a thin layer of lycopodium powder along its length. A convenient way of doing this is to sprinkle the powder on a metre rule, insert the rule in the tube and then invert it. Tape the loudspeaker to the open end of the tube. Use a paper cone to compensate for the different diameters.

2   Set up the apparatus as shown in figure E8. Switch on the signal generator. The speaker will force the air in the tube to vibrate at the same frequency as that produced by the signal generator.

3   Vary the frequency and observe what happens to the powder. Explain why at a particular frequency the powder eventually settles into heaps (piles) at certain positions throughout the length of the tube.

4   Record this frequency and find the average distance between adjacent nodes.

5   Alter the frequency and find another value at which resonance occurs. Repeat step 4.

6   What is the relationship between the distance l between adjacent nodes and the natural frequency f of vibration of the air column?

7   Find an average value for the speed of sound c in the air column at this particular temperature.
Note: You may need to remove the lycopodium powder and re-introduce a thin uniform layer along the length of the tube.

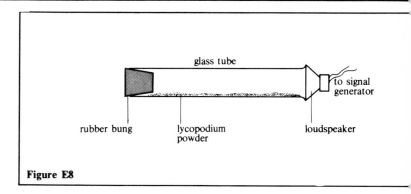

Figure E8

Experiment VW9 Stationary sound waves

Aim
In this experiment you will investigate the formation of a stationary wave pattern in air and measure the speed of sound in free air.

Apparatus
- cathode ray oscilloscope
- signal generator
- loudspeaker
- microphone
- reflecting surface (e.g. drawing board)
- metre rule

A stationary wave pattern
1   Place the loudspeaker and the reflecting surface at opposite ends of a metre rule with the microphone between them, as shown in figure E9. Arrange the loudspeaker and reflecting surface so that the incident wave strikes the reflecting surface at normal incidence.

2   Connect the loudspeaker to the signal generator and the microphone to the Y plates of the c.r.o. Set the signal generator to a frequency of 2 kHz.
Notes: (a) If reflections from the bench surface appear to be a nuisance, place the loudspeaker and reflecting surface on separate supports (e.g. laboratory stools).
(b) Keep the apparatus away from the walls.

3   Move the microphone backwards and forwards between the screen and loudspeaker and observe the trace on the c.r.o. Observe what happens to the amplitude of the c.r.o. trace as you move the microphone. Explain your observations. Why did the points of minimum intensity not fall to zero?

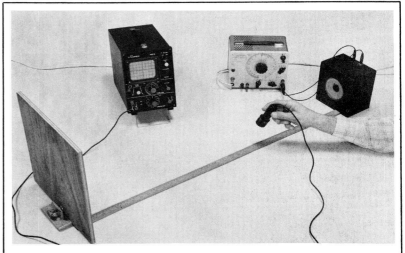

Figure E9

Measurement of λ and calculation of c
1   Locate the positions of the microphone where the c.r.o. trace has minimum amplitude. Obtain a value for the average distance between the nodes and hence calculate the wavelength λ of sound.

2   Repeat step 1 for several other frequencies f.

3   Knowing that $c = f\lambda$, obtain an average value for the speed of sound in free air.

4   What is the main source of error in this experiment?

5   Record the temperature of the air.

6   Compare your value with the theoretical value ($3.3 \times 10^2\,\mathrm{m\,s^{-1}}$ at 273 K).

Experiment VW10 Vibrations in an air column

Aim

To study the resonant vibrations of an air column and measure the speed of sound in air.

Apparatus

- signal generator
- loudspeaker, diameter 60 mm
- resonance tube
- metre rule
- cardboard tube, length 25 cm

Modes of vibration

1 Set up the apparatus as shown in figure E10a. The rate of flow of water from a tap and out to a sink can be varied so that the level of water in the tube can be made to rise and fall slowly or rapidly, or remain at the same level.

2 Fix the water level so that the length of the air column is about 25 cm.

3 Switch on the signal generator and set the frequency at about 50 Hz. Adjust the output control so that the note can just be heard.

4 Gradually increase the frequency until there is a sharp increase in volume. Record this frequency f_1.

5 Continue to increase the frequency until there is a second further increase in volume. Record this frequency f_2.

6 Repeat step 5 and record a third frequency f_3.

7 Explain your observations using the terms fundamental frequency, resonance, harmonic, overtone. What is the relationship between f_1 and f_2, and between f_1 and f_3?

8 Repeat steps 3, 4, 5 and 6 for an open pipe (e.g., a cardboard tube of fixed length 25 cm) and comment on your observations.

Speed of sound in air

1 Set the frequency at a fixed value of 1000 Hz. Record the frequency f.

2 Bring the water gradually to the top of the tube. (Take care, in order to prevent the water flowing over the sides of the tube!)

3 Allow the water level to fall slowly until a sharp increase in the loudness of the sound (resonance) is heard. Make minor adjustments in order to obtain the position of maximum loudness. Measure the length of the air column, repeat the procedure several times and then find the mean value l_1.

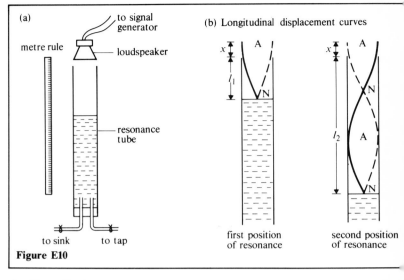

Figure E10

4 Now find the second position of resonance, using the same frequency (the air column will be about three times the length). Obtain mean value l_2 for the length of the air column at which resonance occurs.

5 The diagrams in figure E10b represent the vibrations of the air column in the first and second positions of resonance. Show that the speed of sound c in air is given by $c = 2f(l_2 - l_1)$. Use your results to calculate a value for the speed of sound in air.

6 Repeat steps 2 and 3 with at least four other lower frequencies. Find a mean value of the length l of the resonating air column in each case.

7 Plot a graph of l (y-axis) against $1/f$ (x-axis).

8 Use your graph to find (i) a mean value for the speed of sound in air at this temperature, and (ii) the end-correction of the pipe.

9 Measure the diameter of the pipe. Calculate the ratio of the end-correction to the diameter of the pipe.

Experiment VW11 Waves through holes

Aim

In this experiment you will investigate the effects produced when light passes through small apertures.

Apparatus

- 12 V, 24 W line filament lamp
- SBC holder
- 12 V a.c. supply
- translucent screen
- lens, converging, $f = 50$ cm
- filters (red and green)
- metal foil
- copper wire, 36 s.w.g.
- 2 razor blades
- scissors
- rubber bands
- cardboard
- (optional) adjustable slit, screw controlled

1   Make a very small hole in a piece of aluminium foil. A suitable size for the hole is obtained by using copper wire, 36 s.w.g. First stretch the copper until it breaks and then hold one of the broken ends in between your fingers a few mm from the end and pierce the foil firmly. Hold the pin hole to your eye and look at a 'point source' of light 3 m away in a darkened room. What do you observe?

Note: A 'point source' is an idealised source, to which a bulb with a small filament or a line filament approximates when it illuminates a small hole in a screen placed in front of the lamp.

2   View the source through slightly larger pin holes made using a pin or thicker wire. Does the source of light look smaller when the hole is smaller? Describe the changes you observe for different size holes.

3   Make a narrow slit between the edges of two razor blades as shown in figure E11a. Look at the slit against an illuminated background like a window and adjust the blades so that the edges form as narrow and parallel-sided a slit as possible. In a darkened room, view a line filament lamp through the narrow slit held near your eye, parallel to the filament and at least 3 m from it. Do your observations through holes and slits support the idea of the wave theory of light? Give a reason for your answer.

4   The use of a lens will enable diffraction effects to be observed on a screen. Arrange the apparatus as shown in figure E11b, but without the adjustable slit. Place the lens midway between the lamp and screen which are just over 2 m apart. Place a vertical slit in front of the lamp and parallel to the filament. Move the screen until an image of the slit is focused on the screen.

Place the adjustable slit near to the lens and parallel to the slit source and observe the pattern on the screen. A big stop (a card with 2 cm diameter hole) provides a way of cutting out light which has not passed through the slit and the best position for it must be found by trial and error. Observe the pattern produced on the screen when light passes through a fine slit.

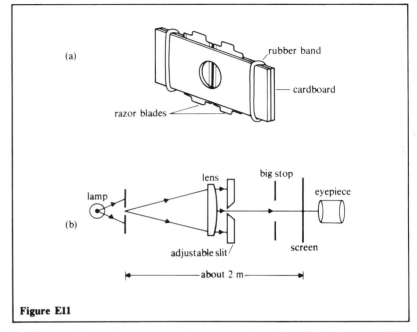

Figure E11

5   Record how the pattern changes as the slit width changes. The pattern can be seen in more detail if a lower power eyepiece is used. The eyepiece can be moved so that it is focused on the translucent screen and then the screen can be removed and fine focusing of the eyepiece completed. The lamp may have to be adjusted so that light falls centrally on the eyepiece lens.

6   Place first a red and then a green filter in front of the light source, and say how the pattern changes.

Note: If you have difficulty in obtaining a pattern on the screen check
(a) that light from the source is falling on the adjustable slit (move the source slit if necessary),
(b) that light from the slit source is entering the eyepiece (check this by removing the adjustable slit and holding a card in front of the eyepiece).

Experiment VW12 Resolving power

Aim
This experiment shows that what we see depends on the colour of the light used and the size of the hole we look through.

Apparatus
- multiple light source
- narrow slit
- red, green and blue filters
- white card

Viewing through a slit

1   Cover the multiple light source (figure E12) with a green filter and look at it through a narrow slit 3 m from the lamp. Adjust the width of the slit until the lamp can just be seen as separate lights and not as a continuous strip.

2   Without changing the slit width or your viewing position, observe the effect when the green filter is replaced by a blue filter and then a red one. Comment on your results.

Resolving detail with the eye

1   Rule two black parallel lines 2 mm apart on a white card. Illuminate the card well. Find the greatest distance at which you can distinguish the two black lines.

2   Calculate the angular separation between two objects which you can just resolve. Compare your results with others in the group and comment on any differences.

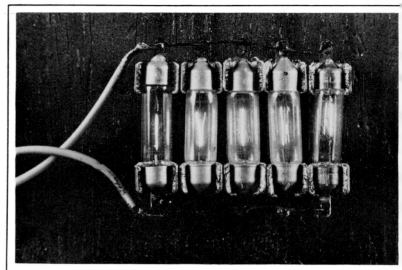

Figure E12

Experiment VW13 Waves past obstacles

Aim
In this experiment, the diffraction of ripples and light waves due to obstacles is observed.

Apparatus
- ripple tank
- hand stroboscope
- point source of light
- screen
- magnifying glass
- pin

Water waves past obstacles

1   A vibrating wooden bar is used to produce plane waves, and an obstacle (e.g. a metal cylinder) is used to form a diffraction pattern. Notice how a shadow is produced behind the obstacle but observe how diffraction produces a 'healing' of the waves and the waves join up again beyond the obstacle (figure E13).

2   The length of the shadow (or healing distance) L_0 is approximately D^2/λ where D is the width of the obstacle and λ is the wavelength of light. Use a hand stroboscope to freeze the wave motion and measure the wavelength of the projected ripples λ and the length of the projected shadow. Does the width of the projected obstacle agree with the above expression?

Note: This method is used in measuring the size of atomic nuclei by finding their 'diffraction cross-section'.

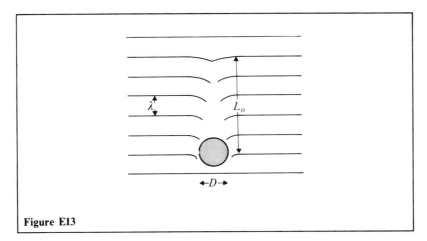

Figure E13

Light waves past obstacles

This next section indicates how you can apparently see through an opaque object. The diffraction of light produces surprising results.

1   Fix a pin three metres away from a bright point source and observe the diffraction pattern on a translucent screen placed 25 cm in front of your eye in a dark room. First place the screen 5 m from the obstacle and observe the diffraction pattern. Is there any light in the centre of the pattern?

2   Move the screen to about 5 cm behind the obstacle and observe the pattern (you will need a magnifying glass for this). Is the centre dark? If so, the screen must be in the region where a shadow is found.

3   For a pin of width 0.5 mm the waves heal up after 50 cm. What will be the length of the shadow region behind a hair of width 0.05 mm? You can look at the diffraction pattern of a hair to check your prediction.

4   As the viewing distance increases, you will observe the shadow change from being dense black to one in which you can see fringes. Which part of the shadow is brightest in this case? (For much larger viewing distances, it is difficult to see any shadow because the waves have completely healed up.)

Experiment VW14 Observing diffraction patterns and measuring wavelength

Aim

In this experiment you will observe the patterns produced by fine and coarse gratings and use a fine grating to measure the wavelength of light.

Apparatus

- coarse grating, approx. 1000 lines per cm
- fine grating, approx. 6000 lines per cm
- line filament lamp and holder
- metre rule
- red filter

Note: The grating you will use is a transmission grating which uses a thin plastic sheet whose surface is moulded so that it transmits light through slits between non-transmitting grooves or ridges.

1 Look at a filament lamp through a coarse grating (1000 lines per cm). (Keep the distance from source to grating large so that nearly plane waves pass through the grating.) What difference do you observe between the zero order maximum and maxima of other orders? Does your observation confirm that different colours of light have different wavelengths? Which colour has the longest wavelength?

2 Now using a fine grating you will concentrate your attention on one maximum (the first order) and on one colour (red). Set up the apparatus as shown in figure E14. The grating is placed 1–2 metres from the lamp and held so that its slits are vertical. A red filter is placed in the light path and a metre rule stands on edge, as shown.

3 With one eye closed, move your head so that you can see the first order red maximum. You will also be able to see the ruler. A vertical pointer (a pin held by your partner or by plasticine) can be moved until it coincides with the middle of the red first order maximum. Measure x, the distance of the pointer from the line of the incident wave.

4 Calculate sin θ and so obtain a value for the wavelength of the red light (you will need to know the number of lines per cm).

5 Estimate the percentage error in your value for λ. (A more precise method using a spectrometer is mentioned in section 3.3.)

6 Observe a point source through two gratings arranged so that their slits are 90° to each other. What happens to the pattern as one grating is rotated about the direction of the incident light?

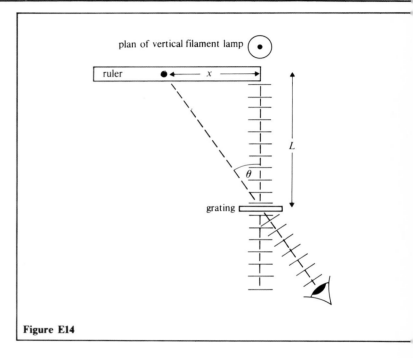

Figure E14

7 You can observe similar effects by using the fine mesh of a handkerchief pulled taut, or by observing a distant point source through a stretched umbrella, or by observing a street light through net curtains. Pull the mesh diagonally and record the change you observe.

xperiment VW15 Observing spectra

Aim

You will compare the spectra of different light sources and note the differences between spectra produced by a grating and a prism.

Apparatus

- fine diffraction grating (3000 lines per cm)
- glass prism
- neon discharge tube (and hydrogen discharge tube, if available)
- e.h.t. supply
- bunsen burner
- red and green filters
- filament lamp and supply
- salt or a sodium pencil

1 Connect the e.h.t. supply to a neon discharge tube set up vertically. Look through the grating at a discharge tube placed as far away as possible. (The grating lines must be parallel to the source, e.g. both vertical.) If other discharge tubes are available, observe the spectra of these sources. How many different wavelengths of light does the source emit? Give a reason for your answer.

2 Now look at the spectrum emitted by glowing sodium atoms. Glowing sodium vapour can be observed if salt is sprinkled in a bunsen flame or a piece of blotting paper soaked in strong brine is wrapped round the burner and projects a little above the top. Does the grating separate light from glowing sodium into several colours? Suggest a reason for your answer.

3 Look at bright white light from a glowing filament lamp and a fluorescent tube through the grating. Record the changes you observe when red and green filters are placed in the beam.

4 Observe the spectrum produced when light from a distant line filament lamp passes through a prism. Hold the prism a few centimetres from your eye with the parallel edges of the prism also parallel to the filament. Rotate the prism until the spectrum is observed. Which colour is dispersed most by the prism? What difference do you observe between the spectrum produced by a prism and that produced by a grating?

5 (Optional)
You can make a simple spectroscope and look at the sun's spectrum using it (figure E15.2).
Note: You must never look directly at the sun but at a piece of white paper illuminated by sunlight.

Do you detect any differences between the sun's spectrum and that of a glowing filament lamp?

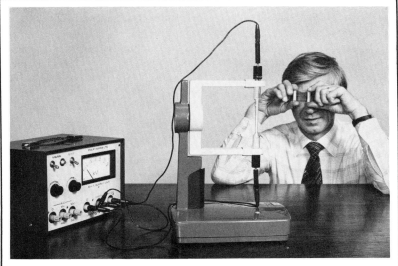

Figure E15.1

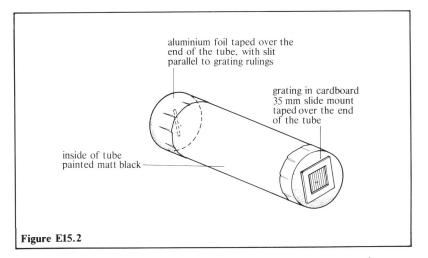

aluminium foil taped over the end of the tube, with slit parallel to grating rulings

grating in cardboard 35 mm slide mount taped over the end of the tube

inside of tube painted matt black

Figure E15.2

Experiment VW16 Lloyd's mirror interference

Aim

An interference pattern is produced by superposition of two light waves from the same small source, one wave being reflected at a shallow angle from a plane surface and the other wave travelling directly from source to observer.

Apparatus

- m.e.s. lampholder with connectors
- flash lamp bulb (2.5 V, 0.3 A)
- plasticine
- microscope slide
- hand lens
- red and green filters
- 1.5 V cell and cell holder

1   Arrange the apparatus as shown in figure E16 with the lamp filament horizontal. Mount the slide on plasticine so that it is between 0.5 m and 1 m from the lamp and arranged horizontally at the same level as the filament. Connect the lamp to the cell.

2   Look along the slide to the lamp and tilt the slide until the image of the filament due to reflection is as close as possible to the filament seen directly.

3   Now look with the hand lens at the back edge of the slide, getting this edge in focus. Equally spaced fringes should be visible.

4   Record your answers to the following questions.
(a) What changes in the number of fringes observed and the spacing of the fringes are produced by placing a red filter and a green filter in front of the hand lens?
(b) What other factors affect the fringe spacing? Explain your answers.
(c) Does the edge of the reflecting surface near your eye lie where a dark or a bright fringe would be? What does this indicate?
(d) What suggestions can you make for improving the quality of the fringe pattern?

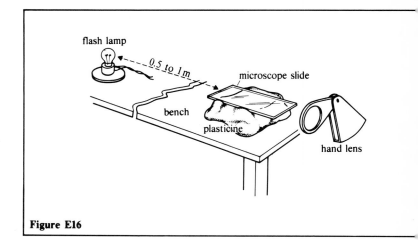

Figure E16

Aim

In this experiment you will investigate how the polarisation of 3 cm radio waves can be analysed and changed.

Apparatus

3 cm wave transmitter
3 cm wave receiver
metal grille
audio amplifier and
loudspeaker (optional)

The transmitter transmits radio waves of wavelength about 3 cm and these radio waves can be detected by a diode and a meter. Radio waves can be used to carry an audio frequency signal, as happens when radio waves are used to broadcast speech and music. These 3 cm waves can carry an audio frequency signal and an amplifier and speaker attached to the receiver will emit a sound which will indicate the amplitude of the radio waves being received.

The grille has metal rods, about 1.5 cm apart, joined by insulating ends. The grille acts as a selective absorber of radio waves. If the rods are vertical and are placed in a vertical electric field, charges will flow along the rods producing forced oscillations of electrons in the rods, and the wave energy is absorbed. The grille acts as an absorber of all waves with electric vibrations parallel to the grille wires.

1   Set up the transmitter T and receiver R as shown in figure E17, without the grille. Observe what happens when R is rotated through 90° in the direction shown. Does the result suggest that the wave from the transmitter is plane-polarised or unpolarised?

2   Insert the grille and observe the effect of rotating it about an axis joining R and T,
(a) when R and T are placed as shown,
(b) when T and R are 'crossed', i.e. with T lying on its side.

3   Use your results to find out
(a) the plane of vibration of the electric waves from the transmitter,
(b) the plane of the electric vibration of waves which the receiver detects.

4   How it is possible with the help of the grille to receive waves in a receiver which is 'crossed' with the transmitter?

5   The grille is *not* a diffraction grating. Can you suggest any reason why this statement seems obviously true?

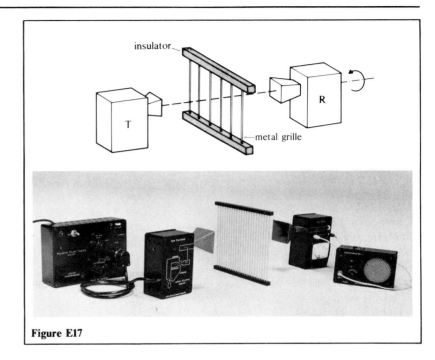

Figure E17

Experiment VW18 Polarising light waves

Aim
In this experiment plane-polarised light is produced by different methods and analysed by Polaroid to obtain evidence that light is a transverse wave.

Apparatus
- lamp
- 2 Polaroid sheets (or 2 pairs of Polaroid sunglasses)
- small sheets of glass, metal and polythene)
- transparent tank
- slide projector

1 Look at a light source through a piece of Polaroid (figure E18.1). Rotate the Polaroid about an axis parallel to the beam. Does this affect the intensity of the light transmitted?

2 Fix one piece of Polaroid over the light source and observe the effect of rotating the second Polaroid. What happens to the light intensity transmitted?

3 What conclusions can you make from your experiments about the difference between light from the lamp and light transmitted by Polaroid? Explain why the first piece of Polaroid is called the polariser and say how the second Polaroid can analyse the light and detect the plane of polarisation.

4 Using *one* piece of Polaroid as an analyser, look at light from the lamp which is reflected (i) from the bench; (ii) from a sheet of glass; (iii) from a metal plate or the shining metal surface of a knife; (iv) from a polythene sheet.

Is there any polarisation of the reflected beam?
Does the angle at which the light is reflected have any effect on wh. you observe?
What kind of materials produce some polarisation at reflection? Wh. kind does not? (The essential difference may be an electrical one sin light is an electromagnetic wave.)

5 Fill the transparent tank with water to which one drop of milk h been added. The milk produces a suspension of tiny particles of fat the water. (Too much milk would produce more than one scatterin encounter for the light and the effect of scattering by single particl would not be seen.) The diagram (figure E18.2) shows where th Polaroid is placed to observe the light which is scattered through 90 What has happened to the light scattered through 90°?
Explain, with the help of a diagram and by consulting your referen books, how you can account for your result, assuming that light wav must have an electric field vibrating across the direction of propaga tion.

6 In step 5 you examined the effect of a single scattering encounter. light travels through a sheet of waxed paper it will undergo multipl scatterings and reflections. Place a small piece of waxed paper betwee crossed Polaroids. Say what you observe and suggest a possible expl nation.

7 What evidence has been provided in steps 1 to 5 that light is transverse wave?

Figure E18.1

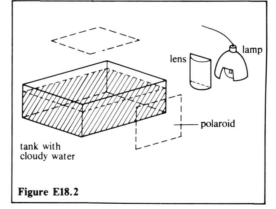

tank with
cloudy water

Figure E18.2

\im

olarised light is used to
vestigate stress in transparent
aterials.

\pparatus

light source
2 pieces of Polaroid
transparent adhesive tape
microscope slide
polythene
red filter

1   Set up a light source and two crossed Polaroids separated by a few centimetres. Take 10 cm of transparent adhesive tape, get a firm grip of the ends and give it a good stretch. Stick it on a microscope slide and trim the ends. View the light transmitted through the specimen when it is placed between the crossed Polaroids. Rotate the specimen and note any colour changes.

Note: The colour you see will depend on the stress in the stretched tape (a uniform colour will indicate that you have pulled it uniformly). The colour effect is produced by double refraction in the film and the speed of one of the refracted plane-polarised waves is determined by the stress in the film. The observed effect of double refraction changes with the stress and with the thickness of the stressed plastic. In the next section you can observe the colour sequence obtained in a stressed film of varying thickness.

2   Take about 25 cm of tape and pull it until it looks pale yellow between crossed Polaroids. Now add successive layers to the slide, building up the thickness in steps (see figure E19.1). Record the colour sequence as the thickness increases.

Note: The same colour sequence will indicate increasing stress in a film of equal thickness, and you can observe this in the following sections.

3   Tear a piece of polythene from a sheet and examine it between crossed Polaroids. (Stress has been produced by the tear which has become permanent.)

4   Observe and record the colour changes produced as you steadily stretch the polythene between crossed Polaroids. Compare the sequence with that obtained in step 2.

5   Take two strips of transparent tape. Cut notches in one and punch a hole in the other (figure E19.2). Stretch the tape, fix it on a slide, and observe the stress patterns using white light and red light. Draw a sketch showing the regions of 'stress concentration', indicated by the concentration of isochromatic (same colour) fringes.

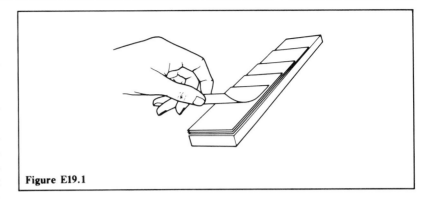

Figure E19.1

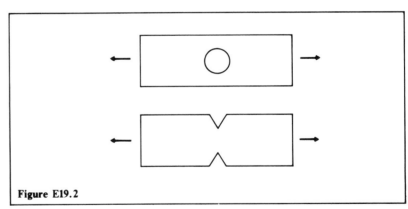

Figure E19.2

Experiment VW20 A simple polarimeter

Aim
Optical activity in sugar solution is observed and the factors on which it depends are investigated.

Apparatus
- 250 ml beaker
- jam jar or sauce bottle
- 2 Polaroid sheets
- green filter
- sugar
- bunsen burner
- tablespoon

1   Put 200 g of sugar in a beaker and add 125 ml of water. Heat gently to dissolve. When it has all dissolved, put it on one side to cool.

2   Meanwhile, fill a sauce bottle or jam jar with water and clamp it vertically over a small light source (see figure E20). Place a piece of Polaroid between the light and the bottle and another Polaroid above the mouth of the bottle. Look at the light source through the water and rotate the upper Polaroid until darkness is produced. Fix the upper Polaroid in this position and remove the bottle of water. Does the removal of the water produce any observable change?

3   Now substitute a bottle of sugar solution with the Polaroids still in the crossed position. What do you see now? Can the light be reduced to zero by turning the top Polaroid? What has happened to the plane of polarisation?

4   Does the amount of rotation produced by the sugar solution depend on the colour of the light? Give evidence for your answer.

5   Do you expect the rotation to depend on the length of solution through which the light passes? Put a green filter over the bottle and test the effect of length of solution on the rotation. Record your results.

6   Test whether the rotation produced by the same length of sugar solution changes if the solution concentration is reduced and record your results.

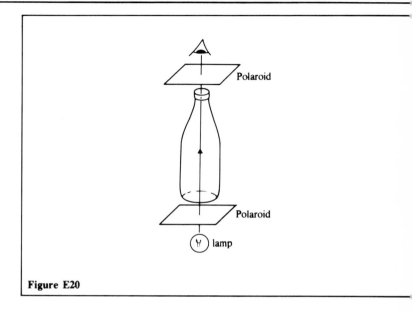

Figure E20

Answers

Chapter 1

1.1 (a) The tension in the spring is proportional to its extension. When the mass moves towards the equilibrium position the extension decreases, hence the pull of the spring on the mass will decrease. Thus the resultant force (which is directed to the left) will decrease.
(b) Because the system has inertia.
(c) The spring is now being compressed. The push of the spring on the load (which provides the restoring force) is now acting to the right.
(d) (i) The kinetic energy increases to a maximum value at the equilibrium position and then decreases. It is zero when the displacement is a maximum. (ii) The potential energy decreases to zero at the equilibrium position and then increases. It is a maximum when the displacement is a maximum.
(e) Because energy is lost from the system. The amplitude will gradually decrease owing to the frictional forces (air resistance) which oppose the moving system. This energy appears as an increase in the internal energy of the surroundings, also internal energy in the spring.

1.2 Shortest time of vibration: springs in parallel. The stiffness factor is doubled, therefore restoring force per unit displacement is increased and the system will take less time to complete one vibration.
Longest time of vibration: springs in series. The stiffness factor is halved, therefore restoring force per unit displacement is decreased and the system will take more time to complete one vibration.

1.3 (a) Because the spring obeys Hooke's law, double the displacement means twice the restoring force because the tension in the spring is proportional to the extension.
(b) It is doubled.
(c) It is doubled.
(d) The load travels twice the distance but, on average, travels twice as fast, so it needs just the same time.

1.4 (a) The springs in figure 1.5b are stiffer.
(b) It is twice as great as before (same distance in half the time).
(c) The acceleration of the second oscillator is four times larger than that of the first oscillator.
(d) The force constant is four times larger for the second oscillator.
(e) $T^2 \propto \dfrac{1}{k}$
(f) Decrease the mass.
(g) The mass would have to be increased by a factor of 4.
(h) $T^2 \propto m$

1.5 (a) (i) Displacement is zero at O, has its maximum positive (downwards) value at A, and its maximum negative (upwards) value at B. (ii) Velocity is maximum at O, and may be in either direction, and is zero at A and B. (iii) Acceleration is zero at O, has its maximum negative (upwards) value at A and its maximum positive (downwards) value at B.
(b) The acceleration and the displacement are always in opposite directions.

1.6 (a) $T = mg$
(b) (i) Upwards, (ii) $T_1 - mg$, (iii) it decreases.
(c) The tension ($T_1 - mg$) corresponds to an extension x; force required is kx, in size.
(d) This follows from Newton's second law.
(e) Upwards, decreasing as the mass approaches O.

1.7 (a) The acceleration is directly proportional to *the distance from the equilibrium position.*
(b) The acceleration is always directed towards *the equilibrium position.*

1.9 For such an object the greater the displacement the greater is the acceleration in a positive direction (i.e. away from the equilibrium position). The velocity of the object will get progressively larger—it will never return to its starting position.

1.15 (a) (i) $x = a \sin \omega t$ (ii) $\dot{x} = a \omega \cos \omega t$
(iii) $\ddot{x} = - a \omega^2 \sin \omega t$
(b) (i) $\dot{x} = \pm \omega (a^2 - x^2)^{\frac{1}{2}}$ (ii) $\ddot{x} = - \omega^2 x$

1.16 The graphs are shown in figure 1.21.

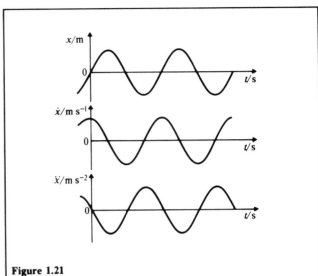

Figure 1.21

1.17   The graph is shown in figure 1.22.

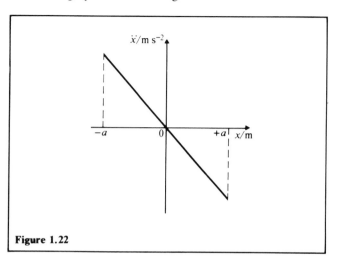

Figure 1.22

1.19   (a) 0.05 m
(b) 0.50 s. Use $T = 2\pi/\omega$ and $\omega = 4\pi$ s^{-1}
(c) 0.20π m s^{-1} (maximum velocity is given by $+ a\omega$)
(d) $0.80\pi^2$ m s^{-2}

1.20 $x = a \cos \omega t$, $\dot{x} = - a\omega \sin \omega t$, $\ddot{x} = - a\omega^2 \cos \omega t$.

1.21   (i) The phase difference is $\pi/2$ rad, the time difference is $T/4$, and velocity leads displacement. (ii) The phase difference is $\pi/2$ rad, the time difference is $T/4$, and acceleration leads velocity. (iii) The phase difference is π rad, the time difference is $T/2$.

1.22   (a) $T/4$ or $\pi/2\omega$
(b) $x = a \cos \omega t_1$
(c) $t = t_1 + \pi/2\omega$ (t is time from O, t_1 is time from O$_1$).
(d) $x = a \sin (\omega t_1 + \pi/2)$, for any angle $\sin (\theta + \pi/2) = \cos \theta$.

1.23   The motion described by $x = a \sin (\omega t + \phi)$ is *not in phase* with that described by $x = a \sin \omega t$. It is out of phase by angle ϕ[radian] or time ϕ/ω. The plus sign indicates that this motion *leads* by time ϕ/ω and so the graph is displaced to the left. (If the motion was described by $x = a \sin (\omega t - \phi)$, the graph curve would be displaced to the right. This motion would be said to *lag*.)

1.25   (a) The mass m of the load and the force constant k of the spring.
(b) The dimensions of ω^2 are those of acceleration ÷ displacement, or $[T^{-2}]$. Since force is equal to mass × acceleration, its dimensions are $[MLT^{-2}]$, therefore the dimensions of k (force per unit extension) are $[MT^{-2}]$.

The dimensions of $\dfrac{k}{m}$ are $[MT^{-2}/M]$ or $[T^{-2}]$.

(c) $\omega^2 = \dfrac{k}{m}$, and $T = \dfrac{2\pi}{\omega}$

Thus $T = 2\pi \sqrt{\dfrac{m}{k}}$

1.26   (a) 5.0π cm s^{-1} upwards
(b) $2.5 \pi^2$ cm s^{-2} towards O.

1.27   0.9 s.
Each spring is depressed 12 mm by a force of 150 N (one quarter of the man's weight),

therefore k for each spring $= \dfrac{150 \text{ N}}{12 \times 10^{-3} \text{ m}}$
$= 1.25 \times 10^4$ N m^{-1}

Each spring is loaded with a mass of 265 kg,

therefore period $T = 2\pi \sqrt{\dfrac{m}{k}} = 2\pi \sqrt{\left(\dfrac{265}{1.25 \times 10^4}\right)}$ s

Alternatively consider four springs in parallel as equivalent to one spring carrying the whole car.

Then $k = \dfrac{600 \text{ N}}{12 \times 10^{-3} \text{ m}}$, so $T = 2\pi \sqrt{\left(\dfrac{1060}{5 \times 10^4}\right)}$ s

The springs at front and back may not be equivalent. They may have different periods of vibration, resulting in a more complex movement. The mass may not be evenly distributed. There may be more mass at the front, or at the back, depending on the position of the engine. The simple model gives the frequency of vibration in a vertical plane only. Without the dampers the car would give an uncomfortable ride.

1.29   At maximum displacement the pendulum bob has maximum p.e. and zero k.e. During the first quarter of the vibration the p.e. decreases and is transformed continually to k.e. which is a maximum when the bob moves through the equilibrium position. In this position the p.e. is a minimum (zero if we take the equilibrium position to be our arbitrary zero). During the second quarter, the k.e. changes continually to p.e., which is a maximum when the bob is at its extreme position. The process is repeated during the third and fourth quarters of the vibration.

1.30 $\dot{x}_{max} = 4\sqrt{1.25}$ m s^{-1}
$\omega = \sqrt{\dfrac{10}{0.8}}$ s^{-1}, and $\dot{x}_{max} = a\omega$

1.33   (a) $E_k = \frac{1}{2} m\dot{x}^2 = \frac{1}{2} ma^2\omega^2 \cos^2 \omega t$

$E_p = \frac{1}{2} m\omega^2 x^2 = \frac{1}{2} ma^2\omega^2 \sin^2 \omega t$

(b) $E_k + E_p = \frac{1}{2} ma^2\omega^2 (\sin^2 \omega t + \cos^2 \omega t) = \frac{1}{2} ma^2\omega^2$
(since $\sin^2 \omega t + \cos^2 \omega t = 1$)

1.34   The graphs are shown in figure 1.23.

1.35   (a) The graphs are shown in figure 1.24.
(b) The frequency of the energy variation is twice that of the motion because k.e. is always positive and has a value of zero twice in each cycle of this motion. In mathematical terms, $E_k \propto \cos^2 \omega t$.

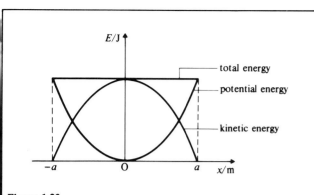

Figure 1.23

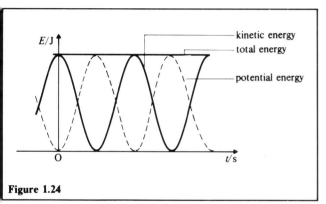

Figure 1.24

1.36 (a) 2.5×10^{-2} J
p.e. at max. displacement = average force × displacement.
Force required to produce a
  displacement of 5.0 cm = 20 N m^{-1} × 0.050 m = 1.00 N
Therefore E_p = 0.50 N × 0.050 m

(b) $+ \sqrt{0.10}$ m s^{-1}
k.e. (max) = 2.5×10^{-2} J
so $\frac{1}{2} \times 0.50$ kg × $\dot{x}^2_{max}$ = 2.5×10^{-2} J

(c) 4.3 cm
$\frac{1}{4}$ k.e. (max) = k.e. (at displacement x)

$\frac{1}{4} (\frac{1}{2} m \omega^2 a^2) = \frac{1}{2} m \omega^2 (a^2 - x^2)$
Rearranging, we have
$x = \frac{\sqrt{3}}{2} a$, so $x = \frac{\sqrt{3}}{2} \times 5.0$ cm

1.37 (a) This is due to resistive forces, i.e. forces which oppose the motion of the oscillating system, such as air resistance.
(b) The energy is dissipated to the surroundings, causing an increase in the internal energy, and to the internal energy of the system.

1.39 Lightly damped: simple pendulum swinging in air, or mass on spring in air.
Heavily damped: car suspension system, or simple pendulum with cardboard vane attached.

1.41 The shock absorbers on a car critically damp the suspension system to prevent the car 'bouncing'. Instruments such as balances and electrical meters are critically damped (sometimes referred to as dead-beat) so that the pointer comes quickly to the correct position without oscillating.

1.42 3/4 of the energy was dissipated.
Energy is proportional to amplitude squared, so
$\frac{\text{initial energy}}{\text{final energy}} = \frac{16}{4} = \frac{4}{1}$

1.43 The loudspeaker must respond to rapid changes in the driving frequency. The energy of one frequency must be quickly propagated so that it does not affect the next. This requires heavy damping. A lightly damped system also produces sharp resonance (see figure 1.18) and a lightly damped speaker would produce undesirably loud notes at particular resonant frequencies. Also its aim is to radiate sound energy, i.e. it is simply an energy transducer.

Chapter 2
2.1 (a) No.
(b) Yes.
(c) No.
(d) Yes.
(e) No (this is not, however, a universal rule for waves, because it is not true for waves which are amplitude dependent).

2.2 If the tension is greater, then the force tending to restore the trolley to its equilibrium position will be greater and so will push the pulse along at a faster speed. If the mass is greater, the trolley's inertia will be greater and the pulse will move more slowly.

2.4 (a) The dimensional equation is
$[L \ T^{-1}] = [M \ L \ T^{-2}]^x . [M \ L^{-1}]^y$
Equating respective indices on each side,
for [L], $1 = x - y$
for [M], $0 = x + y$
for [T], $-1 = -2x$
Thus $x = \frac{1}{2}$ and $y = -\frac{1}{2}$

(b) The speed of the pulse will increase as it travels down the whip. The mass per unit length μ decreases in the direction in which the pulse is travelling, therefore, since $c \propto 1/\mu^{\frac{1}{2}}$, the speed increases.

2.5 (a) Speed of pulse is 45 m s^{-1}. Time taken is 0.44 s.
$T = 10$ N, $\mu = \dfrac{100 \times 10^{-3} \text{ kg}}{20 \text{ m}} = 5 \times 10^{-3}$ kg m^{-1}

$c = \sqrt{\dfrac{10 \text{ N}}{5 \times 10^{-3} \text{ kg m}^{-1}}}$

$c = 45$ m s^{-1}

(b) Cross-sectional area is 1.1×10^{-6} m^2. Consider a wire of length l and cross-sectional area A.

$\rho = \dfrac{m}{V} = \dfrac{m}{Al}$ therefore $\mu = \rho A$

$c = \sqrt{\dfrac{T}{\mu}} = \sqrt{\dfrac{T}{\rho A}}$

therefore $A = \dfrac{T}{c^2 \rho}$

2.7 (a) Speed of sound in aluminium is 5.1×10^3 m s^{-1}.
Use $c = \sqrt{E/\rho}$, where E is the Young modulus.

$$c = \sqrt{\frac{7.0 \times 10^{10}\ \text{N m}^{-2}}{2.7 \times 10^3\ \text{kg m}^{-3}}}$$

$c = 5.1 \times 10^3$ m s^{-1}

(b) The Young modulus of steel is approximately three times that of aluminium.

(c) The bulk modulus of sea water is 2.1×10^9 N m^{-2} (Pa).
Use $c = \sqrt{K/\rho}$, where K is the bulk modulus.
Therefore $K = c^2\rho$

$K = (1.45 \times 10^3\ \text{m s}^{-1})^2\ (1.02 \times 10^3\ \text{kg m}^{-3})$
$\quad = 2.1 \times 10^9$ N m^{-2}

2.8 (a) $c = x/\Delta t$

(b) $v = \dfrac{\Delta x}{2\,\Delta t}$

(c) $m = \rho V = \rho A x$

(d) $\Delta p = mv = \dfrac{\rho A x\ \Delta x}{2\,\Delta t}$

(e) $\dfrac{F}{2} = \dfrac{\rho A x\ \Delta x}{2(\Delta t)^2}$

(f) $F = \dfrac{E\,A\ \Delta x}{x}$

(g) $\dfrac{E\,A\ \Delta x}{x} = \dfrac{\rho A x\ \Delta x}{(\Delta t)^2}$

$E = \dfrac{\rho x^2}{(\Delta t)^2} = \rho c^2$

therefore $c = \sqrt{E/\rho}$

2.9 The dimensions of p are $\left[\dfrac{\text{M L T}^{-2}}{\text{L}^2}\right]$ or $[\text{M L}^{-1}\ \text{T}^{-2}]$.
The dimensions of ρ are $[\text{M L}^{-3}]$.
Hence dimensions of $(p/\rho)^{\frac{1}{2}}$ are

$$\left[\frac{\text{M L}^{-1}\ \text{T}^{-2}}{\text{M L}^{-3}}\right]^{\frac{1}{2}} = [\text{L}^2\ \text{T}^{-2}]^{\frac{1}{2}} = [\text{L T}^{-1}]$$

The dimensions of c are also $[\text{L T}^{-1}]$.

2.11 (a) A 5% change in the speed of sound.
Let c be the speed at temperature T.
Suppose temperature increases by 10%, therefore

$$c_1 = c\sqrt{\frac{110\,T}{100\,T}} = c\sqrt{1.1} = 1.05\,c$$

(b) No change—speed is not dependent upon pressure.

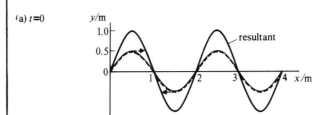
(a) $t=0$

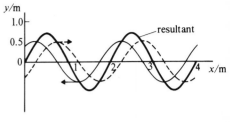
(d) (i) $t=0.5$ s

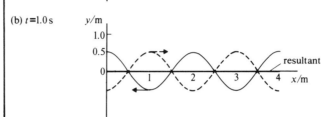
(b) $t=1.0$ s

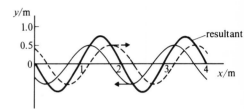
(ii) $t=2.5$ s

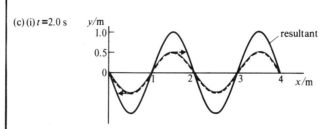
(c) (i) $t=2.0$ s
(ii) $t=3.0$ s

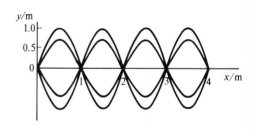
(e)

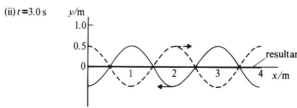

Figure 2.14

2.12 (a) to (e) See figure 2.14.
(f) (i) Points which are 1.0 m, 2.0 m, 3.0 m, and 4.0 m from the point $x = 0$. (ii) Points which are 0.5 m, 1.5 m, 2.5 m, and 3.5 m from the point $x = 0$.
(g) The distance is 1.0 m.
(h) This is half the wavelength of the progressive wave.

2.13 (a) See figure 2.15.
(b) The particles between adjacent nodes appear to move up together and down together (in the case of a transverse stationary wave on a string). They are in phase. The amplitude depends on location between the nodes and varies from zero at a node to a maximum of $2a$ at an antinode, where a is the amplitude of the progressive waves.
(c) Particles on one side are moving up when particles on the other side are moving down. They are in antiphase—there is a phase difference of π rad.

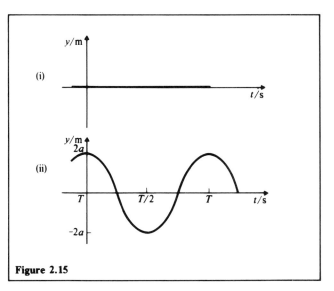

Figure 2.15

2.16 (i) $y = 2a \sin \omega t$
(ii) $y = 2a \cos kx$

2.17 The progressive wave takes a time of $T/2$ to travel along the string to the other end, where there is a phase change of π rad, and a time of $T/2$ to travel back to the other end. On reflection, there is a further phase change. At the start of its second run down the string, the reflected wave has taken a time equal to T and has suffered two phase changes, and therefore it is exactly in phase with the next wave from the source. This reflected wave adds to the next wave; this is repeated in subsequent cycles and a large stationary wave is set up.

2.18 (a) $l = n\dfrac{\lambda}{2}$ therefore $\lambda = 2l/n$

From $c = f\lambda$, $c = f(2l/n)$
therefore $f = n(c/2l)$
(b) The phase difference between the incident and reflected waves will be constantly changing and the resulting superposition will therefore be changing. The string is being subjected to *forced vibrations*.
(c) (i) The amplitude of the reflected waves is less than that of the incident waves, therefore they cannot completely cancel each other.
(ii) The system is damped because energy is being transferred from the string to the surroundings. Damping decreases the sharpness of the resonance peaks (see figure 1.18, chapter 1) and therefore broadens the frequency response, so stationary wave patterns of fairly large amplitude can be obtained at frequencies which are not quite equal to the natural frequency.

2.19 (a) Speed of pulse is 70 m s^{-1}.
Using $c = \sqrt{T/\mu}$

$$c = \sqrt{\dfrac{4.9 \text{ N}}{1.0 \times 10^{-3} \text{ kg m}^{-3}}} = 70 \text{ m s}^{-1}$$

(b) Length of string is 2.1 m.
Using $c = f\lambda$, we have $\lambda = \dfrac{70 \text{ m s}^{-1}}{50 \text{ s}^{-1}} = 1.4 \text{ m}$
Thus distance between consecutive nodes is 0.7 m.

2.20 Speed of sound in carbon dioxide is 264 m s^{-1}.
$\lambda/2 = 0.16$ m, therefore at 289 K
$c = (850 \text{ s}^{-1})(0.32 \text{ m})$
$= 272 \text{ m s}^{-1}$

$$\dfrac{c_{273}}{272 \text{ m s}^{-1}} = \sqrt{\dfrac{273 \text{ K}}{289 \text{ K}}}$$

$c_{273} = 264 \text{ m s}^{-1}$

2.21 (i) The excess pressure is a maximum (above normal pressure).
(ii) The excess pressure is a maximum (below normal pressure).
Note: When the particle displacement is a maximum the excess pressure above or below atmospheric pressure is zero.

2.22 See figure 2.16.

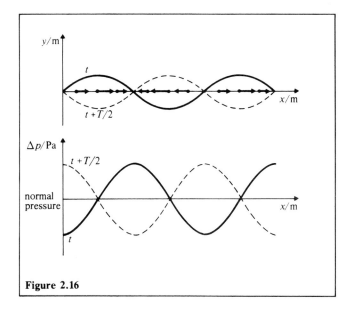

Figure 2.16

2.23 By coupling the vibrating string to a resonator. The air inside a cavity (e.g., a guitar body) and the material of the instrument (the thin wooden body of the guitar) all vibrate producing much greater vibrations in the surrounding air than would be produced by the string alone.

2.25 (a) 1.4×10^3 Hz
(b) 7.0×10^2 Hz
(c) 5.0×10^2 Hz

2.27 (a) The frequency is inversely proportional to the diameter of the wire.
Consider a wire of length l and diameter d,

$$\rho = \frac{m}{V} = \frac{4\,m}{\pi d^2 l}$$

Hence $\mu = \dfrac{\pi d^2 \rho}{4}$

Therefore $f = \dfrac{1}{l}\sqrt{\dfrac{T}{\pi d^2 \rho}}$

(b) 140 N
Substitute values in the equation in (a).

2.28 (a) An alternating transverse force is exerted on the wire, because it is a current carrying conductor in a magnetic field.
Resonance occurs when the natural frequency of the wire is equal to the mains frequency.
(b) 2.5 N

2.29 (a) This is the term which is used to describe the fact that the same note played on different instruments does not sound the same. It depends upon the number of overtones present and their relative intensity.
(b) Fundamental frequency is the lowest frequency obtainable from a string (or pipe).
A harmonic is a note whose frequency is an integral multiple of the fundamental frequency.
An overtone is a note whose frequency is actually obtainable from a string (or pipe).

2.31 f/Hz 256 288 320 341 384 427 480 512

2.32 (a) You can change the length of the string with your finger. For violins, shortening the string by about 1 finger width changes the note by a semitone. Guitars have frets built in to make this easier.
(b) Most stringed instruments have their strings arranged so that their fundamental frequencies are about 5 semitones apart. Thus, a scale can be played by playing 2 or 3 notes on each string before moving to the next.

2.34 (a) (i) The loudness of the note depends upon how hard you blow. (It may be possible to produce a note of higher frequency, i.e. an overtone.)
(ii) Yes. When the length of the air column is increased the frequency of the note decreases.
(b) The pitch of the note changes.

2.38 (a) Length of pipe is 0.52 m.
For a closed pipe, $\lambda/4 = 0.5$ m

$$f = \frac{340 \text{ m s}^{-1}}{2.0 \text{ m}} = 170 \text{ Hz}$$

The other pipe is longer and therefore has a lower frequency. Difference in frequency is 8 Hz.

$$l = \frac{c}{4f} = \frac{340 \text{ m s}^{-1}}{4 \times 162 \text{ s}^{-1}} = 0.52 \text{ m}$$

(b) 425 Hz, 850 Hz, 1275 Hz, 1700 Hz.
For an open pipe, $\lambda/2 = 0.40$ m

$$f = \frac{340 \text{ m s}^{-1}}{0.8 \text{ m}} = 425 \text{ Hz}$$

In an open pipe, all the harmonics are present.

2.39 (a) A graph of l against $1/f$ gives a straight line (figure 2.17).
For the first position of resonance,
$\lambda/4 = l + x$, where x is the end-correction.
Now $c = f\lambda = 4f(l + x)$
Rearranging, $l = (c/4f) - x$
The gradient of the graph is $c/4$ and the negative intercept on the l-axis is x.

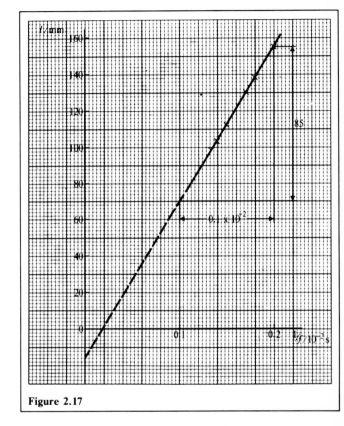

Figure 2.17

(b) The position of the displacement antinode is a short distance x beyond the end of the tube, where x is the end-correction and equals 0.6 × radius of tube.
From the graph, $x = 16$ mm, so the radius of the tube = 27 mm.
(c) Speed of sound at 273 K is 330 m s^{-1}.

Gradient of graph $= \dfrac{85 \times 10^{-3} \text{ m}}{0.1 \times 10^{-2} \text{ s}} = 85 \text{ m s}^{-1}$

thus $c = 4 \times 85$ m s^{-1} = 340 m s^{-1}
Use $c \propto \sqrt{T}$ to correct for temperature.

Chapter 3

3.1 $\dfrac{\lambda_{\text{sound}}}{\lambda_{\text{light}}} = 4 \times 10^6$

3.2 In figure 3.1a the aperture width is just less than a wavelength and the ripples are diffracted through a wide angle. In figure 3.1b the aperture width is about four wavelengths and most of the wave energy travels forward within a small angle around the original incident direction. A small proportion of wave energy is diffracted into the region of the 'shadow' when compared with figure 3.1a. The pattern in figure 3.1b shows strong waves travelling in certain directions with calmer water between these directions.

In figure 3.1c there is no significant diffraction effect for waves travelling through the central region of the wide aperture. Diffraction effects are limited to the part of the wavefront travelling near to the edge of the aperture.

In figure 3.1d the aperture width is of the order of the wavelength and the diffraction pattern is similar to figure 3.1a. The factor which determines the character of each pattern is the factor wavelength/aperture width, or λ/a. If $\lambda/a \approx 1$, waves are diffracted through large angles. If $\lambda/a \ll 1$, no significant diffraction occurs (except at the edges).

Diffraction of light waves at a slit confirms that narrow slits produce waves diffracted through large angles. Fringes are seen in a single slit diffraction pattern of light waves and figure 3.1b shows similar variations in the intensity of ripples.

3.3 (a) Figure 3.2 suggests that a wall of water with vertical faces could exist beyond the barrier. This is impossible, since a sideways force would be exerted on the vertical wall producing sideways spreading. Water waves cannot propagate beyond the barrier without spreading sideways.

(b) If the frequency is increased there is less time for water particles to fall sideways during their vertical oscillations and so there is *less* spreading.

3.4 A line of speakers sending sound through a large slit, e.g. 1 m × 20 cm. Detection could be by microphone and meter or c.r.o.

3.5 (a) Amplitude.

(b) See figure 3.24. The resulting amplitude can be obtained from a graph (figure 3.24a) or by using addition of vectors a_1 and a_2 making angle ϕ (phase difference) with each other (figure 3.24b).

Note: These vectors representing wave amplitude and phase are called phasors and will be used in the Unit *Electromagnetism* for a.c. circuits, but a phasor treatment of wave superposition is not required.

(c) Intensity is proportional to (amplitude)^2.

3.6 (a) Yes; see figure 3.25.

(b) A plane wavefront would be propagated to the right. A new wavefront is always the envelope of all the separate disturbances produced by point sources on the original wavefront (Huygens' principle).

3.7 (a) $a/2$

(b) $\dfrac{a \sin \theta_1}{2}$

(c), (d) and (e) Darkness.

(f) $\lambda = a \sin \theta_1$, or $\sin \theta_1 = \lambda/a$

(g) For angles less than θ_1, the path difference between each pair of strips is less than $\lambda/2$ so the waves do not produce a zero resultant.

(h) The effect of the whole wavefront passing through the slit can be found by adding the effects of pairs of slits $a/4$ apart. Resulting effect: minimum light intensity for $\sin \theta_2 = 2\lambda/a$.

(i) If the waves from two narrow strips $a/6$ apart have a path difference $\lambda/2$ at angle θ_3, then

$\dfrac{a}{6} \sin \theta_3 = \dfrac{\lambda}{2}$, so $\sin \theta_3 = \dfrac{3\lambda}{a}$

3.8 θ is small; most of the light travels straight ahead (rectilinear propagation).

3.9 (i) 0.68 rad or 40°, (ii) π radians or 180°.

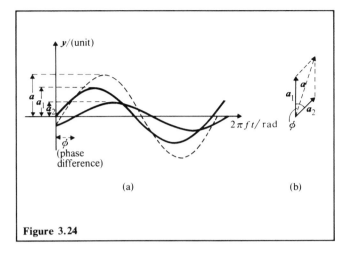

Figure 3.24

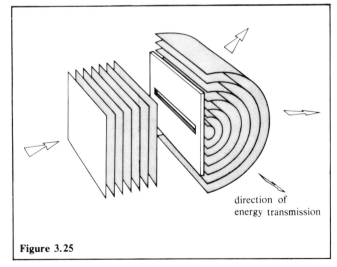

direction of energy transmission

Figure 3.25

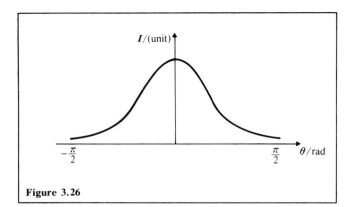

Figure 3.26

3.10 See figure 3.26.

3.11 (a) Figure 3.3e.
(b) Very wide slit or no slit at all (the photograph is of a line source without a diffracting slit).
(c) 2λ ; The widths of the central maxima in figures 3.3c and 3.3d are in the ratio $1:2$, so

width of central maximum $\propto \dfrac{1}{\text{slit width}}$

(d) Yes. In figure 3.6, the angular width of the central maximum $(2\lambda/a)$ is twice the angular separation of adjacent minima (λ/a). In figure 3.3 the width of the central maximum is twice the distance between minima.

3.12 The diffracted waves probably do not overlap. Suggest making the slit separation smaller. Narrower slits give more spread due to diffraction but, if the slits are too narrow, not enough light will pass through to observe the effect. The most appropriate compromise is to have the slits very close together and not too narrow.

3.14 The angular separation of just resolved point objects, θ. If diameter D increases, θ decreases (since $\theta = \lambda/D$), and so the resolving power is increased.

3.15 By admitting only the shortest wavelengths of visible radiation the resolving power of the telescope is increased (θ is decreased, since $\theta = \lambda/D$).

3.16 $x = 2.1$ m
$$\theta = \frac{x}{3.0 \times 10^5\,\text{m}} = \frac{\lambda}{D}$$
$$x = \frac{5.5 \times 10^{-7}\,\text{m}}{7.5 \times 10^{-2}\,\text{m}} \times 3.0 \times 10^5\,\text{m}$$

3.17 (a) 2.5×10^{-4} radian
(b) 8×10^{-6} m
(c) Yes, because the separation of images on the retina is 5×10^{-6} m for objects which are just resolved.
(d) Aberrations of the lens system and chromatic aberration.

3.18 In very bright light the pupil contracts considerably and the resolving power is decreased due to diffraction. Note that the resolving power depends on the size of the aperture both because of diffraction effects and because of aberrations. In less bright light the pupil dilates and increases the aberrations more than it reduces diffraction, hence the quality of the image decreases in dim light. In very dim light the periphery of the retina is used (for greater sensitivity) but in this region there is a lower density of receptors so detailed vision becomes worse.

3.19 (a) 2×10^{-7} radian
(b) 10^{-4} radian
(c) No, the angular separation is less than 3×10^{-4} radian at the eye.
(d) A magnification of 1500 enables the eye to see resolved diffraction patterns of two stars which subtend an angle of 2×10^{-7} radians at the telescope.

3.20 (a) Picture brightness diminishes. A pinhole (diameter 1 mm) admits about one quarter of the light which would be received by the unobstructed pupil.
(b) Picture brightness is decreased (received light reduced to one quarter). Diffraction effects may now reduce the picture definition. The best size for the viewing hole is one which is small enough to remove the 'noise' by making the tiny dots of light fuzzy, but not too small, to ensure that the picture definition is preserved.

3.21 Diffraction of the waves enables the sound to bend round corners and around obstacles (houses). The longer wavelength sounds (low frequency) are diffracted more. The sound 'shadows' are smaller for long waves and the bass notes are more audible.

3.24 $\sin \theta_1 = \lambda/s$, $\sin \theta_2 = 2\lambda/s$
Draw tangents to the zero, first and second order diffracted waves and measure the angles between these tangents. Measure λ and s on the diagram and write down values of λ/s, $2\lambda/s$, $\sin \theta_1$ and $\sin \theta_2$.

3.25 (a) 4.8×10^{-7} m
$$\sin 20° = 0.35 = \frac{\lambda}{1.7 \times 10^{-6}\,\text{m}}$$
also $\sin 45° = \dfrac{2\lambda}{1.7 \times 10^{-6}\,\text{m}}$
(b) Third order maxima are not visible, since $3\lambda/s = 1.05$ and $\sin \theta_3$ must be $\leqslant 1$.
(c) First minima of slit pattern are at $55°$, therefore $\sin 55° = \lambda/a$
$$a = \frac{4.8 \times 10^{-7}}{0.80}\,\text{m}$$
$$= 6.0 \times 10^{-7}\,\text{m}$$

3.26 Increasing the angle of incidence reduces the path difference between light reflected from adjacent slits. Since the gramophone record acts as a very coarse grating only oblique reflection will produce the lower order maxima ($m = 1, 2, 3$ etc.) which are seen as spectra of the fluorescent tube. At smaller angles of incidence higher orders of diffraction maxima are seen, but the overlapping of these orders prevents a clear spectrum being seen. To produce a good spectrum the axis of the tube should be parallel to those grooves which are acting as a grating.

3.27 Angle between second order maxima $= 0.01$ rad, therefore $\theta_2 = 0.005$ rad $\approx \sin \theta_2$
$$s = \frac{2\lambda}{\sin \theta_2} = \frac{12 \times 10^{-7}\,\text{m}}{0.005} = 2.4 \times 10^{-4}\,\text{m}$$
Slits (threads) per metre $= 1/s = 4.2 \times 10^3\,\text{m}^{-1}$

Comprehension exercise

1 Average wavelength of waves along coastline (to determine grating spacing); average amplitude of waves (to decide what length of grating is required for a particular power output). It will be necessary also to know by what factor these quantities vary.

2 Assume that the power of the waves before diffraction is equal to the power of the waves after being focused by diffraction.
Power $\propto I \times l$, where I is the intensity and l the length of the wavefront.
Since $I \propto$ (amplitude)^2,
$a^2 \times 10^4 \text{ m} = (10^2 \times 400) \text{ m}^3$
$a = 2$ m (a realistic value)

3 $AF = D + \lambda$, $BF = D + 2\lambda$, $CF = D + 3\lambda$
The spacing of the gaps will decrease with distance from O.

3.28

(a)	(b)
1 Narrow slit	to produce a line object
2 Converging lens (collimator)	to produce a parallel beam
3 Prism or grating	to disperse the light into its separate wavelengths
4 Focusing lens or telescope	to project an image on a screen to produce an image in the eye

(One lens can be used instead of the separate collimator and focusing lenses.)

3.30 Object is at a distance, therefore nearly plane waves are incident at the grating. The observer's eye is used to focus a diffraction pattern.

3.31 The dispersion by a fine grating is greater than that produced by a prism, so more lines are resolved. The grating can be of the reflection type, which is advantageous in avoiding absorption by a prism (or lenses used with a prism) of infra-red and ultra-violet.

3.32 (a) Dispersion approximately 11°.
$$\sin \theta_1 = \frac{7.0 \times 10^{-7} \text{ m}}{1.7 \times 10^{-6} \text{ m}}$$
θ_1 (red) = 24° 30′, θ_1 (blue) = 13° 45′
(b) θ_2 (red) = 56°
(c) Yes, θ_3 (blue) is 47° 30′ which is less than θ_2 (red).

3.35 The light from the white hot filament is focused on the slit, but two particular wavelengths of yellow light are absorbed by the sodium vapour. This light is re-emitted in all directions by the glowing sodium but the light reaching the slit is deficient in yellow—hence two dark lines appear.

3.36 (a) Continuous emission spectrum with line absorption spectrum.
(b) Dark absorption lines due to absorption by gases in the sun's gas envelope and the earth's atmosphere. The wavelengths are characteristic of the particular gases.
(c) More absorption occurs in the earth's atmosphere when the sun is low in the sky and lines due to atmospheric absorption will appear darker when the sun is low.
(d) Matter in the sun is gaseous but more densely packed together than normal gases. In this dense matter the atoms are undergoing frequent interactions (collisions) with each other. This results in the emission of a continuous spectrum like the radiation from hot solids.

3.37 Frequency is fixed by the energy changes in the source. Wavelength of light changes because the speed changes in different media, but wavelength in vacuum is constant.

3.38 (a) Travel time will increase because the wave speed in the slab is reduced.
(c) nt
(d) $(n - 1)t$
(e) 30 wavelengths
(f) 30 wavelengths
(g) 3.6×10^{-5} m

3.39 (a) Behind the mirror.
(b) P
(c) Zero
(d) Bright.
(e) Insert optically dense slab in the wave travelling to P without reflection.
(f) With white light the central fringe appears white with red edges. Other identifiable fringes are white with red and blue edges (red furthest from the centre). Each wavelength forms a fringe pattern, the red light producing fringes with wider separations, and all these overlap.
(g) Using $m\lambda = dx/D$ (as in Young's experiment, described in the Unit *Wave properties*), $m = 5$. The geometrical path difference at P is five wavelengths, but because of a phase change on reflection there is a dark fringe at P.

3.40 (a) $\lambda/2$
(b) No; phase change for wave 2 only.
(c) Geometrical path difference of $\lambda/2$ and phase change of π rad for wave 2 produces reflected waves in phase.
(d) Dark fringes at O, B and D. Bright fringe at C (and A).

3.41 Wavelength in water is 3/4 wavelength in air, so fringe separation changes to 0.3 mm (since $\theta = \lambda/2x =$ a constant).

3.42 Thickness = 2.3×10^{-5} m

3.44 Fringe pattern shrinks. This is an accurate method of measuring refractive index and can be used for very small quantities.

3.45 Use an optical wedge between two glass slides. One glass slide is kept fixed and the other is attached to the expanding crystal. Count the number of dark fringes, m_1, in the wedge (excluding the zero order dark fringe). (The m th dark fringe is located where the film thickness is $m\lambda/2$.) Heat the crystal and observe the change in the number of dark fringes, m_2. Thickness is now $m_2 \lambda/2$, and

$$\text{expansion} = \frac{(m_2 - m_1)\lambda}{2}$$

3.46 (a) The film drains downwards, with the thinnest part of the film at the top. The film has equal thickness along horizontal lines.
(b) The film is too thin to produce constructive reflection of visible wavelengths. Invisible ultra-violet wavelengths are reflected strongly.

3.47 (a) Whole number of wavelengths ($m\lambda$).
(c) $\lambda_{max} = 6 \times 10^{-7}$ m, yellow.
(d) $\lambda_{max} = \frac{6}{3} \times 10^{-7}$ m, ultra-violet.
(e) (i) $\lambda_{max} = 4.8 \times 10^{-7}$ m for $m = 1$, so green is reflected.
$\lambda_{max} = \frac{4.8}{3} \times 10^{-7}$ m for $m = 2$, so ultra violet is reflected.
The film appears green.

(ii) $\lambda_{max} = 12 \times 10^{-7}$ m for $m = 1$, i.r.
$\lambda_{max} = 4 \times 10^{-7}$ m for $m = 2$, blue.
$\lambda_{max} = \frac{12}{5} \times 10^{-7}$ m for $m = 3$, u.v.

The film appears blue.

Chapter 4

4.1 (Three properties from each group, (a) and (b) below, should be given.)
(a) (i) They transfer energy from place to place.
(ii) They are diffracted.
(iii) They obey the principle of superposition.
(iv) They may undergo a phase change of π on reflection.
(Reflection and refraction are *not* possible answers, since they are not exclusively wave properties.)
(b) (i) They are generated by accelerating particles.
(ii) They do not require a material medium.
(iii) They travel at 3×10^8 m s^{-1} in vacuum.
(iv) They are emitted and absorbed by matter, absorption producing an increase in the internal energy of matter.
(v) They show certain properties which require a photon model.
(c) The frequency of the radiation and hence its wavelength in vacuum.

4.3 (a) The field is in the direction X to Y, and is decreasing.
(b) (i) Clockwise, (ii) B perpendicular to E.

4.4 See figure 4.27.
(a) Horizontal.
(b) In a vertical plane containing line PQR.
(c) Vertical.

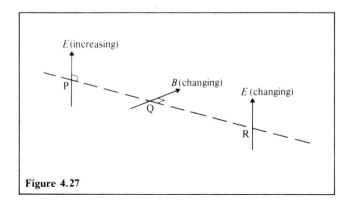

Figure 4.27

4.5 See figure 4.28.

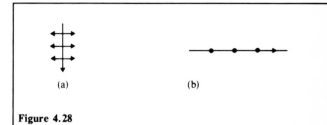

(a)   (b)

Figure 4.28

4.6 (a) The electric field is created *across* the gap, so the plane of the E vibration is parallel to the dipole rods.
(b) $\lambda = \frac{3 \times 10^8 \text{ m s}^{-1}}{10^9 \text{ s}^{-1}} = 30$ cm
(c) No wave detected.
(d) The vertical E vibrations of the receiver can be divided into two components, each equal to $E \sin 45°$, parallel and perpendicular to the rod. The component perpendicular to the rod will be transmitted through the rod. The horizontally polarised component ($E \sin^2 45°$) of this wave will be detected by the receiver.
(e) The diode rectifies the alternating current induced in the receiver circuit. Without the diode the average value of the induced current will be zero, but with the diode in use an average current (not zero) can be recorded on a meter which thus detects the wave.

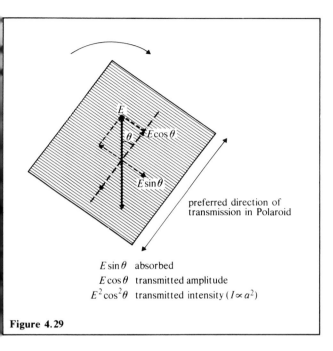

$E \sin\theta$ absorbed
$E \cos\theta$ transmitted amplitude
$E^2 \cos^2\theta$ transmitted intensity ($I \propto a^2$)

Figure 4.29

4.7 See figure 4.29.

4.8 Polaroid headlamp filters and driving glasses are used with the Polaroid arranged so that both glasses and headlamp filters transmit light whose plane of polarisation is in the same diagonal plane for all cars (e.g. at 45° to the vertical and the horizontal off-side direction). Drawing a sketch will help you to visualise the effect. The driver will see clearly the light of his own headlight beam reflected from the road but the oncoming traffic will produce a plane polarised headlight beam which is crossed with respect to the driver's glasses. The oncoming headlights will be very faint; he will detect the car because of the unpolarised beam from the 'side lights'.

4.10 (a) Light reflected from the ground is partially plane-polarised, and much of this light energy can be absorbed by Polaroid to reduce glare.
(b) Polaroid absorbs most of the nearly plane-polarised light reflected from the water surface, but nearly 50% of the unpolarised light coming up through the surface will pass through the Polaroid (see figure 4.30) to show the inside of the river.

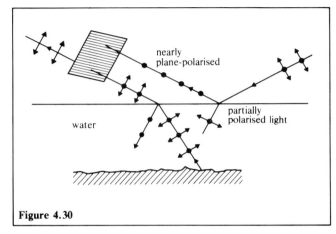

Figure 4.30

4.12 At each glass plate a proportion of the light energy is reflected as a plane-polarised beam and the transmitted energy contains progressively less of one major component until it emerges plane-polarised.

4.13 If light is a transverse vibration, then light scattered through 90° by the atmosphere will be plane-polarised (see experiment VW 18). With the sun on your left or right, look at a patch of sky from which the light to your eye is at right angles to the earth-sun direction. Rotate the Polaroid. If there is extinction in one position the light is plane-polarised.

4.14 The light from a half moon has been turned through 90° at the moon's surface, as a result of reflection and scattering at the surface, and will be nearly plane-polarised.

4.15 A quantum of visible radiation is less than the ionisation energy of a gas and so interaction between gas atoms and light does not produce ionisation. X-ray quanta are able to ionise a gas. As a result of this ionisation, X-ray energy is absorbed by a gas but there is no such absorption of light energy. Light waves are therefore more penetrating in a gas than X-rays.

4.18 A reflection grating, which will be coarser than gratings used for light.

4.19 Reflection. Radio waves with wavelengths of the order of several centimetres.

4.20 (a) Microwaves, if they are generated in oscillating circuits, but this frequency range is shared with infra-red radiation and the latter name could also be used.
(b) Absorption by walls, doors, etc. This is a property characteristic of i.r. radiation and very high frequency microwaves which is not possessed by other radio frequencies.

4.21 (a) 50 cm
(b) 50 m

4.22 At 150 km from the receiver, the sky wave and ground wave have similar amplitudes and they will superpose to produce an interference pattern. If the height of the ionosphere varies, the path difference at the receiver will change. This produces a variation in signal strength at the receiver: one moment it is at a maximum of the pattern and the next at a minimum (nearly zero). Variations in the amplitude of the reflected wave (caused by changes in the ionosphere density) will also produce changes in the amplitude at the receiver. At greater distances, only the sky wave will reach the receiver and the interference effect is eliminated.

4.23 (a) Tobacco smoke particles are smaller than the wavelength of light and blue light is scattered more than red light by these particles. The water drops formed at the spout of a kettle are much larger than visible wavelengths and so all visible wavelengths are scattered significantly—hence the 'steam' is white.

(b) Light from the sun has been scattered in the atmosphere. Since short wavelengths are scattered more than long wavelengths, the blue component of the white light predominates in the scattered light so the sky looks blue. Looking at the sun, unscattered light coming from this direction is therefore deficient in blue. Higher in the atmosphere there is less scattering; as the astronaut rises the sky darkens to deep blue and eventually black; and the sun appears progressively whiter.

(c) Infra-red rays are not scattered much by tiny water particles in the mist because of their longer wavelength.

4.24 A wave travelling directly and a wave reflected from an aircraft will be superposed at the aerial. The path difference will determine the strength of the resultant signal and, as the reflector is moving, the aerial will be alternately a point of maximum and minimum signal strength. At maximum a clear picture will be seen, at minimum the picture becomes distorted or disappears.

4.26 Long waves. The complex information carried by a TV signal can only be carried by very short waves (v.h.f. or u.h.f.) and these waves cannot be diffracted around large obstacles.

4.27 Short waves (microwaves) cannot be diffracted around fair-sized obstacles and do not bend round the curved earth. They must be beamed in straight lines from a transmitter to a receiver 'in line of sight', which re-transmits the signal to the next microwave receiver/transmitter station.

4.29 10^{-8} to 10^{-14} m; 10^{-5} times the wavelength of light; about 10^7 lines per cm (too fine to rule).

(It is, in fact, possible to use a coarser ruled grating with X-rays. Extremely small grazing angles are used and the grating spacing appears 'foreshortened' to rays at grazing incidence. The wavelength of X-rays has been determined using such ruled gratings.)

4.30 (a) and (b) The scattered wavelets superpose constructively in only one direction to produce a plane scattered wavefront which makes the same angle with the Bragg plane as the incident wavefront.

(c) $2d \sin \theta$

(d) $2d \sin \theta$

(e) Path difference $= m\lambda$, where $m = 1, 2, 3, \ldots$

(f) Waves scattered from other equidistant planes will be in phase at the detector.

(g) $2d \sin \theta = m\lambda$

(h) Reflection diffraction grating.

4.31 Using the Bragg law, $\sin \theta = m\lambda/2d$

$\theta_0 = 0$, for $m = 0$

$\theta_1 = \sin^{-1}(3/8) = 22°$, for $m = 1$

$\theta_2 = \sin^{-1}(6/8) = 49°$, for $m = 2$

The peak signals will occur when the angle between T and R is (i) 180° (T and R in line), or (ii) 156° ($180° - 2\theta_1$), or (iii) 82° ($180° - 2\theta_2$).

4.32 (a) $\lambda_A = 2d \sin \theta_A$

$\lambda_A = 9.6 \times 10^{-11}$ m

$\lambda_B = 11.3 \times 10^{-11}$ m

$\lambda_C = 13.2 \times 10^{-11}$ m

(b) Peaks D, E, F are second order diffraction maxima satisfying $\sin \theta = 2\lambda/2d$. G, H, I are third order maxima satisfying $\sin \theta = 3\lambda/2d$.

(c) Spacing of Bragg planes $= d = \dfrac{11.3 \times 10^{-11} \text{ m}}{2 \times \sin 8.4°}$

$= 3.9 \times 10^{-10}$ m

λ_A and λ_C can also be used to calculate d, and the average value can be obtained.

Abbreviations used in the text

Akrill	Akrill, T. B. and Millar, C. J. *Mechanics, vibrations and waves.* John Murray, 1974.
Bolton	Bolton, W. *Patterns in physics.* McGraw Hill, 1974.
Duncan FWA	Duncan, T. *Advanced physics: Fields, waves and atoms.* John Murray, 1975.
Duncan MM	Duncan, T. *Advanced physics: Materials and mechanics.* John Murray, 1973.
Millar	Akrill, T. B., Bennet, G. A. G. and Millar, C. J. *Physics.* Edward Arnold, 1979.
Nelkon	Nelkon, M. and Parker, P. *Advanced level physics.* Heinemann, 3rd edition (SI) 1970, 4th edition 1977.
Wenham	Wenham, E. J. and others. *Physics: concepts and models.* Addison Wesley, 1972.
Whelan	Whelan, P. M. and Hodgson, M. J. *Essential principles of physics.* John Murray, 1978.

Values of physical constants

Quantity	Symbol	Value
Speed of light in vacuo	c	3.00×10^8 m s^{-1}
Permeability of free space	μ_0	$4\pi \times 10^{-7}$ H m^{-1}
Permittivity of free space	ϵ_0	8.85×10^{-12} F m^{-1}

Standard symbols used in this Unit

Symbol	Quantity	Unit	Symbol for unit
$\ddot{x}$	acceleration	metre per second squared	m s^{-2}
A	area	metre squared	m^2
a	amplitude	metre	m
θ	angle	radian, degree	rad, °
ω	angular velocity	radian per second	rad s^{-1}
K	bulk modulus	pascal, newton per metre squared	Pa, N m^{-2}
ρ	density	kilogram per metre cubed	kg m^{-3}
d	diameter	metre	m
E, W	energy	joule	J
F	force	newton	N
k	force constant	newton per metre	N m^{-1}
f	frequency	hertz	Hz
E_k	kinetic energy	joule	J
l	length	metre	m
$\dot{x}$	linear velocity	metre per second	m s^{-1}
m	mass	kilogram	kg
T	period	second	s
ϕ	phase angle	radian, degree	rad, °
E_p	potential energy	joule	J
p	pressure	pascal, newton per metre squared	Pa, N m^{-2}
r	radius	metre	m
γ	ratio of principal molar heat capacities (gas)	dimensionless	
n	refractive index	dimensionless	
c	speed of waves	metre per second	m s^{-1}
T	temperature (thermodynamic)	kelvin	K
t	time	second	s
λ	wavelength	metre	m
E	Young modulus	pascal, newton per metre squared	Pa, N m^{-2}

Acknowledgments

Thanks are due to the following, who have kindly permitted the reproduction of copyright photographs: page 4, Prof. F. B. Farquharson; page 22, Mary Evans Picture Library; page 40, Guillemin; page 60, University of Manchester, Jodrell Bank Laboratory; figure 1.3, Kodansha; figure 1.7b, T. Duncan; figures 2.4, 3.23, Education Development Centre; figure 3.1, from *Ripple Tank Studies of Wave Motion* by W. Llowarch, published by Oxford University Press, © O.U.P.; figures 3.3, 3.9, 3.10, G.R. Graham; figure 3.21a and b, Prof. S. Tolansky; figure 4.18b, Trustees of the British Museum (Natural History).

Thanks are due to the following for permission to reproduce copyright material: question 1.4, the Longman Group Ltd.; Comprehension exercise page 52. This first appeared in New Scientist, London, the weekly review of science and technology; Comprehension exercise and questions page 57, University of London, University Entrance and Schools Examinations Council.

Project team   John Bausor (Director)
               Leslie Beckett
               Allan Covell
               David Davies
               Martin Hollins

Printed in Great Britain by Martin's of Berwick

0 7195 3602 2 (Student's guide)
0 7195 3603 0 (Teacher's guide)